Raising Good Parents

A Guide to Your Baby's First Year

ISBN Number: 978-1-936634-28-6
LOC Number: 2013956442

*Thank you to my partners at
Pediatric Associates of Orlando
for their ongoing support*

*A special thanks to Dan Kitts for helping
me start my website and encouraging
me to write this book.*

*This book is dedicated to my wife
Maggie. Thank you for gifting me the
time and supporting my effort to
complete this project.*

Table of Contents

Introduction...i

First Year Timeline vi

Newborn 1

Feeding.. 2

Sleep.. 16

Circumcision Care.. 18

Fever... 27

Two Weeks 29

Sleep.. 30

Feeding.. 46

Fussiness 50

Circumcision Care.. 54

Plagiocephaly 58

Two Months...61

Vaccines.. 61

Growth chart basics.. 64

Sleep.. 67

Fever.. 73

Four Months 75

Feeding 76

Sleep 91

Six Months 95

Feeding 95

Sleep 99

Acetaminophen and Ibuprofen 108

Nine Months.................................. 110

Feeding 111

Discipline..117

Twelve Months 127

Feeding 128

Weaning Pacifiers.......................................138

Final Thoughts 140

Bibliography................................. 141

Introduction

As a general pediatrician, I see parents make many of the same avoidable mistakes. To address their concerns, parents often consult family, friends, books and internet websites. Often, the questions and advice are of poor quality and fail to address the issues.

Grandparents have traditionally served to pass on pearls of parental wisdom to the next generation. Unfortunately, modern grandparents are not viewed as the primary source of parenting advice. In the last fifty years, our society has witnessed high divorce rates, lack of extended family involvement and a less traditional definition of family. This instability has left many young parents without support and without clear parenting role models. Previously, children grew up observing and sharing in parental responsibilities. Modern parents are, on average, older than parents were a generation ago. As parents age, so do grandparents. As grandparents age, their time tested advice is distorted by memory or often considered obsolete. This marginalization of grandparental advice can be attributed to a breakdown in the traditional "family unit" and increased number of years from parent to grandparent.

In search of solid parenting advice, modern parents often turn to "parenting experts." Unfortunately, this "expert" advice is often trendy and unproven. Often, the most educated, well-meaning parents are sucked into these "revolutionary," untested ideas. The best parenting ideas have been time tested and are grandmother approved. Good parenting is love-motivated, hard work and is tirelessly consistent. There are no shortcuts. Think of the best parents you know. They don't count to three for discipline. They don't let their kids eat junk. They don't buy into all the "expert" advice. They are calm, consistent, use traditional methods and set a good example.

As parents, we completely love our children despite their actions. We need, however, to teach our children actions that will be embraced in the world.

We all want our children to be healthy and well behaved. The foundation for both a healthy lifestyle and behavior are laid in the first year of life. Getting off to the right start is critical. Families that are able to address issues during the first year of life seem to possess (or develop) the skills to address later issues. The same parents that can't get their son to sleep through the night also can't get him to eat a healthy diet.

Motivated by a few families in my practice, I started my own parenting advice website, gregorygordonmd.com. After several months of answering parents' emails, it became clear that many parents are struggling with the same problems. The major first year issues are feeding, sleeping, discipline and circumcision care. New parents seem unaware of how and when to address these common parenting pitfalls. Knowledge and anticipation can prevent these challenges in the first year of life. The ideas and concepts presented in this book are not new or unique. They are honest, straight forward, traditional approaches to address the most common parenting issues. They have been repetitively tested in my practice and in our home.

Pediatricians face the challenge of taking care of both children and their parents. The time constraints of modern medicine often limit what can be accomplished at an office visit. We tend to focus on the "doctor" stuff and neglect the "parent" stuff. Experienced guidance is essential; parenting is only part instinct. Good advice is critical to raising good parents.

Disclaimer

I do not claim to be a perfect parent, have perfect children or have all the answers. As a new parent, you will be inundated with parenting advice. Much of the advice is impractical or contradicts other advice. Over our first eighteen years of parenting, Maggie and I found success with some strategies and came to embrace certain principles. These are the strategies and principles that I would like to share.

The sleep training methods described in this book apply to healthy, full term children. In particular, the sections on spacing out feedings and crying it out do not apply to premature babies, children with growth concerns or other health issues.

The advice in this book does not pertain to all parents or all children. Seek the advice of your child's pediatrician if you have questions.

Organization

The chapters in this book coincide with the first year check up ages: Newborn, two weeks, two months, four months, six months, nine months and twelve months. The book is organized primarily by age and then subdivided by topic. Topics in each section are intended to help prevent future problems. Parent questions are used in each section to highlight important topics. Often the ages of children in the parent questions do not correlate with the chapter age. These questions are included not based on age of the child in question, but on the relevance of the topic.

After eight children, fifteen years of pediatric medicine and four years of answering questions on my parenting website, I see what parenting issues families frequently fail to address. There are many books that tell what children should do at each age, but there really isn't a book that tells what *parents* should be doing at each age. The primary goal of this book is to help parents address and avoid the most common first year pitfalls.

The timeline shown on the following two pages is intended to highlight these areas. It is a timeline of when parents need to address common first year issues. Hopefully, it will serve as a quick-reference guide to show parents when they need to act to avoid common problems. The items on the timeline correlate with check boxes seen throughout the book.

First Year

When parents need to address

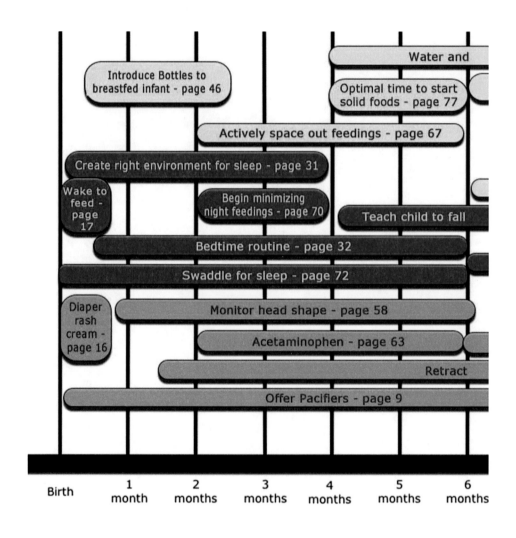

Water and

Introduce Bottles to breastfed infant - page 46

Optimal time to start solid foods - page 77

Actively space out feedings - page 67

Create right environment for sleep - page 31

Wake to feed - page 17

Begin minimizing night feedings - page 70

Teach child to fall

Bedtime routine - page 32

Swaddle for sleep - page 72

Diaper rash cream - page 16

Monitor head shape - page 58

Acetaminophen - page 63

Retract

Offer Pacifiers - page 9

Birth | 1 month | 2 months | 3 months | 4 months | 5 months | 6 months

Timeline
common first year issues

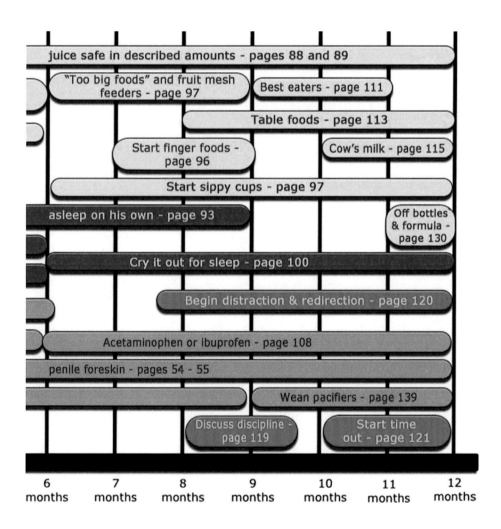

juice safe in described amounts - pages 88 and 89						

"Too big foods" and fruit mesh feeders - page 97

Best eaters - page 111

Table foods - page 113

Start finger foods - page 96

Cow's milk - page 115

Start sippy cups - page 97

asleep on his own - page 93

Off bottles & formula - page 130

Cry it out for sleep - page 100

Begin distraction & redirection - page 120

Acetaminophen or ibuprofen - page 108

penile foreskin - pages 54 - 55

Wean pacifiers - page 139

Discuss discipline - page 119

Start time out - page 121

| 6 months | 7 months | 8 months | 9 months | 10 months | 11 months | 12 months |

Newborn

By the time our first child was born, I had amassed a spectacular resume for the position of fatherhood: I babysat as a teen, was a camp counselor for five years, taught a kindergarten church school class, graduated from medical school and had begun a top rate pediatric residency. Shortly after our daughter arrived, I began to see my knowledge deficiencies.

Our first child was born three months into my residency. After her birth, Maggie focused on nursing, while I assumed the role of chief diaper changer. Breastfeeding started out great. Maggie seemed to know just what to do, and our daughter latched on well. My job was to change diapers and record both stools and voids. Our daughter made plenty of poopy diapers, but she was not urinating. Both our nurse and her assistant stopped by frequently to ask if she had voided. Our daughter's lack of urine was beginning to worry us. As the time for discharge approached, our nurse informed us that she would need to be urinating better in order to go home. Finally, our nurse decided to double check me. She put on a pair of gloves and began pulling my daughter's "stool only" diapers out of the garbage. Our nurse began to chuckle, as every diaper was wet with urine. I was accustom to the heavy, soaked diaper of older children, not the light, barely-wet diapers of a newborn. I was a doctor who had spent my life working with children, but I clearly had a lot to learn.

Newborn Feeding

Starting Breastfeeding

Truthfully, this is a hard subject for a "guy" to feel like an expert. I have never breastfed a child (though several of my children have tried). It could be argued that this is not the best way to start this book. After much deliberation, I realized feeding is the first major challenge that parents face with a new child, and therefore is the right place to start. In this section, I will rely heavily on the knowledge and expertise of my wife, Maggie.

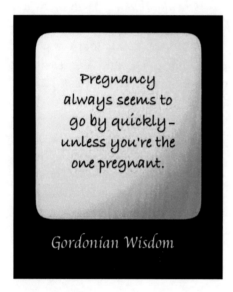

Pregnancy always seems to go by quickly – unless you're the one pregnant.

Gordonian Wisdom

How long should we nurse our baby?

Breastfeeding is best and mothers who can, should try to nurse their babies. Currently, the American Academy of Pediatrics recommends nursing for the first twelve months, or longer. Despite these recommendations, the average American mother nurses for three months. Nursing takes time and commitment. In practice, I often see mothers who end breastfeeding as they return to work and to their "regular" lives.

Many breastfeeding advocates argue that mothers should nurse well beyond the first year of age. These statements are supported by the fact that, in many countries, mothers nurse for at least two years. While a true statement, I do not interpret this fact as solid evidence of what is "best" or "intended." In many countries, there are no safe alternatives. Nursing is clearly safer than contaminated water sources and unstable food supply.

In practice, I (and many other pediatricians) struggle to balance between encouraging breastfeeding and understanding when a mother is simply unable or unwilling to nurse her child. This is a delicate balance. Often, simple questions produce tears from physically and emotionally exhausted mothers.

All of our children were breastfed - with varied duration and success. Our first five children were exclusively breastfed. At some point, our children seemed to lose interest in breastfeeding. Our philosophy was to breastfeed until they naturally moved on. As they became more interested in solid foods and mealtimes, their drive to nurse slowly decreased. Our first five quit nursing between ten and twenty-four months.

Our breastfeeding story took a dramatic turn with the birth of our sixth child, Bennett. Ben was our sickest child at birth. At thirty-seven weeks gestation, our baby stopped moving. After an urgent evaluation with Maggie's OB, we decided to induce. He arrived 6 lbs 5 oz, but was quickly transferred to the neonatal intensive care unit secondary to breathing problems. After a week of oxygen, IV antibiotics and tube feedings, we were finally able to bring him home.

Maggie and I thought Ben would be fine; if we could just get him home. Unfortunately, we were wrong. He was unable to successfully nurse despite:

- lactation consultation
- purchased and rented breast pumps
- a home scale and frequent weighings
- multiple supplements
- oral motor therapy
- huge sacrifices of time and energy.

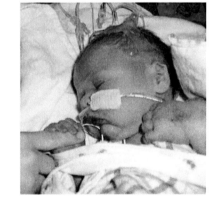

We had given our best and failed. Initially, we blamed Bennett. "There must be something different or wrong with him." "Maybe it was the tube feedings?" The answer became clear after nursing failures with our seventh and eighth children. Maggie nursed these later children as long as she could, but they relied on formula for the majority of their calories. Was it our increasing age? Was it our busy lifestyle? We will never know. Sometimes breastfeeding just doesn't work out.

Breastfeeding and cessation of breastfeeding are often tough issues for mothers. Frequently, they are torn by their personal desires, physical stamina and societal expectations. I advise my patients to try breastfeeding and see how it goes. For most mothers, nursing works. But breastfeeding is not for everyone. Breastfeeding should end when the child has weaned himself, or when it has become such a struggle that it is interfering with family relationships.

How will I know my milk is in?

In the first few days of life, new mothers nurse to provide their newborn with a milk called colostrum. This early milk is yellow in color and small in quantity. For most

If you are uncertain whether your milk has "come in," it probably has not.

new mothers, their milk "comes in" three to five days after delivery. In my experience, even first time mothers know when their milk has come in.

When a mother's milk "comes in" there are usually three changes:
1) Mothers report their breasts feel engorged.
2) The yellow colostrum gradually changes to an increased volume of whiter milk. As the color of the milk becomes whiter, so does an infant's spit up. Sometimes white milk pools at the corners of the baby's mouth while he is suckling.
3) As the volume of milk increases, newborns will swallow more frequently and seem more satisfied after nursing sessions.

After birth, infants will have dark, tarry, sticky stools called meconium for three to five days. As feeding is established, the stools will gradually lighten. Normal infant stools are the color and consistency of guacamole or seedy dijon mustard. In the first two weeks of life, stools are a sign the child is well hydrated and getting milk. If the mother of a breastfed newborn calls and reports her child has not stooled in 24 to 48 hours, my immediate concern is that the child is not getting adequate nutrition. This is an important patient to bring in, weigh and evaluate the same day. On the other hand, if a well growing and non-fussy 3-week-old has not stooled in two to three days, I would not be as concerned. Normally, I would have the family closely monitor for an additional 48 hours before encouraging an office visit.

Weight (Going Down)

Newborns typically lose weight in the first three or four days of life. Weight loss occurs in formula fed newborns too, but not to the same extent as in breastfed infants. A new mother's early milk, colostrum, seems more designed to help a newborn's immune system than to stimulate growth. Colostrum has relatively little fat and is only produced in small quantities.

New mothers often struggle with their baby's weight loss despite their best efforts. A "normal" weight loss is up to 10 percent of birthweight. Most pediatricians see newborns shortly after hospital discharge to monitor the baby's weight loss and feeding success. Only after the mother's breast milk comes in does the infant begin to grow. Newborns should regain their birth weight by 10 to 14 days.

Common Breastfeeding Problems

A common mistake occurs when the infant latches onto only the tip of the nipple, rather than taking the whole areola (the darker pigment surrounding the nipple) in his mouth. This causes increased pain for the mother and only a limited supply of milk for the child. Infants should be encouraged to open wide and latch on to the whole pigmented areola. This is done by manually compressing the breast while enticing the baby to root and open his mouth.

In the first several weeks, newborns are often sleepy and therefore difficult to feed. This can be exacerbated when children are jaundiced (yellow). Often, children require physical stimuli to wake them up during nursing.

Common methods are changing the diaper, flicking the feet, undressing the baby, or rubbing the spine. We have even resorted to using a wet washcloth applied to the baby's feet on our sleepiest newborns. Maggie's favorite technique, however, is simply pausing feedings to make eye contact and interact with the baby. These pauses work by removing the newborn from the warm skin-to-skin contact and last only a few minutes.

The Pain of Nursing

Early on, breastfeeding simply hurts. Usually, after three weeks of breastfeeding, the pain resolves and nursing is no longer painful. When asked, Maggie will often tell new mothers to try nursing for at least six weeks to decide if it is right for them.

While OBs may provide narcotic pain medication for maternal comfort, these medications can be excreted in the breast milk and make sleepy newborns even sleepier. These medications should be minimized to improve feeding and alertness.

> **According to Maggie, "Talking about the pain and difficulty of breastfeeding makes the whole thing sound awful, but it is satisfying to have that closeness with your infant and know you are doing your best."**

My wife's favorite breastfeeding comfort measure uses heated rice. Take uncooked rice and place it in a thin sock. Heat the rice filled sock in the microwave until warm. Apply the warm rice filled sock directly to your breast or simply place in your bra. The rice retains its heat and provides some topical relief.

How often should I nurse my newborn?

Feeding intervals are standardly measured from the start of one feed to the start of the next feed. Newborns usually need to be fed every two to three hours. As children age, spacing out their feedings will help them sleep better. By four months, children should be fed every three to four hours.

From birth until a mother's milk comes in, it often feels like nursing is constant. Newborns should be put to breast every one to three hours as tolerated. These frequent feedings help establish a mother's milk supply. Once a mother's milk is established, babies should be fed every two to three hours day and night. For full term healthy babies, nighttime wakings for feedings should end when the baby is two weeks old.

Should I nurse on both sides during each nursing session?

Like so many parenting topics, you will hear many opinions on this; equal time on each breast or only on one side per feeding. Prolonged nursing on one breast provides more of the fat-rich hind milk. Maggie and I recommend feeding the first 75% of their feeding on the initial breast. This method reasonably allows the child to get enough of the fat-rich hind milk. The subsequent feeding should begin on the breast where the last feeding ended. In spite of these efforts, most babies develop a "favorite" breast and make their mothers temporarily lopsided.

How do I know he is getting enough milk?

It is difficult to know if your baby is getting enough breast milk. As a mother's milk comes in, the milk is whiter and the newborn will swallow more. Stool color changes from dark meconium to dijon mustard. The best way to know if a newborn is getting enough milk is to follow the child's weight. Newborns getting adequate nutrition will grow quickly - often half to one ounce a day.

How long should nursing sessions last?

Newborns typically will nurse for 45 minutes. As both baby and mother gain experience, these sessions get quicker. By two to three months of age, babies will often only need fifteen to twenty minutes to get a full feeding.

Do pacifiers interfere with nursing?

Parent question:

I am breastfeeding my son. He is six weeks old. He seems, however, to spend a lot of time on the breast and is just pacifying (incidentally, he doesn't take a pacifier). Is this okay? How long should he spend there?

I am pro-pacifier. Early in my career, I was uncertain about pacifier use as the American Academy of Pediatrics (AAP) was not in favor of their use. Pacifiers reportedly interfered with breastfeeding. When our first born began to use my wife as a pacifier, we found pacifiers to be helpful tools. Today, the AAP encourages pacifiers as they have been shown to reduce the risk of SIDS.

The time required for breastfeeding varies for every mother and child. Lactation experts often talk about the first ten minutes as the most critical. In general, nursing should take much less time as he gets older. The key missing fact is your son's weight. If he is struggling to gain weight, he may need every minute. If you are uncertain about his growth, it is best to get him weighed and evaluated.

I suspect you are right and he is pacifying on you. While it is not wrong to let him nurse for prolonged periods, it's impractical. If you choose to try a pacifier, it will take some persistence on your part. In the beginning, pacifiers frequently fall out and need to be replaced every few minutes. Given time, he will develop coordinated, lower maintenance pacifier habits.

The Gordon Pacifier Program

Pacifiers are effective tools to help with fussing babies. New parents are often uncertain about using pacifiers, as they have seen older children who still rely on pacifiers, or heard that pacifiers interfere with breastfeeding. When managed correctly, pacifiers help with fussiness and have little downside.

We rely on pacifiers so much that we pack pacifiers to bring to the hospital. Pacifiers were previously discouraged and even banned from hospitals because it was thought that pacifiers interfered with breastfeeding. Our family experience and current medical evidence refutes this. Some physicians and lactation specialists still prefer to wait until breastfeeding has been fully established before offering pacifiers.

During the first few weeks of life, most infants can only keep a pacifier in for four or five sucks. New parents often interpret this weak coordinated suck as a pacifier dislike. Given time and practice, your child will be able to keep a pacifier in longer.

 During the first year, let your child have a pacifier.

Pacifiers are an essential part of our family bedtime routine (during the first two years). After six months, we often leave several pacifiers in our child's crib to increase his likelihood of finding one in the middle of the night.

I fear early removal of the pacifier may lead to thumb sucking. Between 9 to 12 months old, we begin to wean our children of their pacifiers. At this time, pacifiers should be reserved for bedtime, car seats and stressful situations. After the child falls asleep, the pacifier should be removed from his mouth. Between 18 and 24 months, the pacifier should be permanently taken away. See more about weaning pacifiers in the 12 month section.

Breastfeeding when Sick

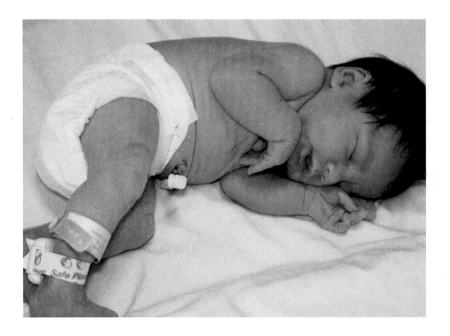

Parent Question:

Should I stop breastfeeding my 11-day-old if I have a stomach bug?

This is an important time to continue nursing. Formula will never be able to replicate the immune protection provided by breast milk. Stomach bugs (viruses that cause gastroenteritis) typically enter an individual through their gastrointestinal tract. Breast milk contains Immunoglobulin A, which protects against this sort of infection, meaning your breast milk provides your infant's best protection against this virus.

Many parents question if they should hold or feed their children when sick, reasoning that they do not want to expose loved ones to their illness. However, chances are that your baby is already exposed.

You may, however, need to supplement with formula while you are sick. Depending on your level of illness and hydration status, the sickness could decrease your milk supply. Drink lots of extra fluids to make up for increased losses. If needed, have your husband or other caretaker offer one to two ounces of formula or pumped breast milk.

Take your infant to the doctor if he gets sick or if he is feeding less.

Starting Formula

What is the best infant formula?

Choosing the right formula for your child is a lot like choosing a car:

1) There are many makes and models and different offerings around the world.
2) A few basic functional "types" - truck versus van versus sedan.
3) Option packages with confusing advertising and advice.

Formula offerings vary in different areas of the world. The big formula companies offer a complete formula line to meet a multitude of needs. In the United States, the biggest formula companies are Ross, who makes Similac®, Mead Johnson, which produces Enfamil®, and Gerber, the makers of Good Start®.

Given time, these offerings will change. These formula giants continually fund research to improve their products. It is often argued whether the small tweaks made to their ingredients are significant improvements, or simply ways to distinguish their formula in a crowded marketplace.

Start by Picking the Base Model

These various offerings can be placed into four basic types of formulas:

1) Regular (Cow's Milk Based)
2) Soy or Lactose Free
3) Added Rice
4) Elemental (Pre-digested)

Like average breast milk, most formulas contain 20 kcal per ounce. These formulas differ predominately on proteins, carbohydrates and fats. The vitamins and mineral content is essentially the same. Good formulas contain vitamin D and a full amount of iron. Do not use a low iron formula unless directed by your physician.

Regular (Cow's Milk Based)

Most children should start with a cow's milk based formula. These "regular" formulas are man's best approximation of human breast milk.

They are based on cow's milk, therefore contain cow's milk protein. The cow's milk proteins are heat treated to make them easier to digest. Despite this, some children do not tolerate cow's milk protein. "Cow's milk protein intolerance" is a common reason that some children cannot drink this type of formula.

Soy or Lactose Free

Soy, "gentle" and "sensitive" formulas all developed as alternatives to cow's milk based formulas. When children do not tolerate cow's milk formulas, these are typically the next type of formula recommended.

Many of these formulas are "lactose-free" versions of a cow's milk formula. Manufacturers actually remove the lactose sugar. Both cow's milk formulas and breast milk contain lactose as their primary carbohydrate source. It is extremely rare that children are born truly lactose intolerant.

Despite this, many children thrive and seem happier on these lactose free formulas.

Soy formulas are also lactose free but do not contain cow's milk protein, they contain soy protein isolate. This is a reasonable option for children thought to have cow's milk protein intolerance. Unfortunately, some children who are intolerant to cow's milk protein are also intolerant to soy protein. Some families prefer soy formulas as they are not produced with animal products.

Added Rice (AR or spit up formulas)

Added Rice formulas are designed to help babies with reflux (GERD or gastroesophageal reflux disease). Rice starch is combined with either a regular or sensitive formula. By adding the rice starch, they are thicker and help children keep the formula in their stomach.

Traditionally, children with reflux are fed formula with rice cereal added by their parents. The formula and rice cereal mixtures are thick and may fail to pass through regular nipples. Often, families learn to enlarge the nipple holes to allow the mixture to pass freely. The already added rice starch formulas are easier to prepare and readily pass through standard nipples.

Elemental (Pre-digested)

Elemental formulas are intended for the worst cases of formula intolerance. Their proteins are broken into amino acids, and they use only simple sugars. When changing a child to an elemental formula, I warn my patients about the number one side effect - diarrhea. These formulas do cost more and smell horrid.

Option Packages

Formula companies often boast new features. Current advertised features include: Probiotics, Prebiotics, DHA/ARA, Lutein and Nucleotides. These featured ingredients will change probably before this book is published. These features are the latest additions to already proven products. They are part scientific research and part formula company marketing. The trick is to decide if they are right for your child.

Formula Preparations

Formulas are available as ready-to-feed, powder and concentrate.

Ready-to-Feed

Ready-to-Feed formula is the easiest but most expensive way to purchase formula. The container only needs to be opened and poured into a bottle. Hospitals often provide two ounce bottles of ready-to-feed formula. Simply remove the cap and screw on a nipple. Parents love these bottles as they are incredibly easy. I suggest saving any of these bottles for night feedings or for traveling.

Powder

Powder formula is the least expensive way to purchase formula. Large quantities can be stored in a small space. Mix one scoop per two ounces of non-fluoridated water (non-fluoridated water should be used for the first six months of life). Shaking up the bottle and feeding it directly to your baby results in your baby swallowing air bubbles. Swallowed air bubbles will cause gas or burping. After you shake up a bottle, wait a minute before feeding it to your baby.

Concentrate

Concentrate is halfway between Ready-to-Feed and powder. It's like mixing Campbell's Soup®. One can of concentrate per one can of water. It is easier than powder, but less expensive than Ready-to-Feed.

How much milk does a newborn need each day?

Newborns need 100 to 120 kcal per kilogram per day to grow. Knowing that commercial formulas and the average women's breast milk contain 20 kcal per ounce a table can be derived.

The table on the next page shows general ranges that can be used as guidelines. Your child's growth is the best way to evaluate his or her milk intake. In my practice, if children are developing and growing well, I usually do not take a detailed history on milk intake. Like breastfed infants, formula fed infants usually lose weight in the first few days of life. All newborns should be back to their birth weight by 10 to 14 days old.

Child's Weight	Range of Breast Milk or Formula needed per day
6 pounds / 2.7 kg	13 to 16 ounces / 384 to 473 ml
6.5 pounds / 3.0 kg	14 to 17 ounces / 414 to 502 ml
7 pounds / 3.2 kg	16 to 19 ounces / 473 to 561 ml
7.5 pounds / 3.4 kg	17 to 20 ounces / 502 to 591 ml
8 pounds / 3.6 kg	18 to 22 ounces / 532 to 651 ml
8.5 pounds / 3.9 kg	19 to 23 ounces / 561 to 680 ml
9 pounds / 4.1 kg	20 to 24 ounces / 591 to 710 ml
9.5 pounds / 4.3 kg	22 to 26 ounces / 651 to 769 ml
10 pounds / 4.5 kg	23 to 27 ounces / 680 to 798 ml

gregorygordonmd.com

During the first two to three weeks of life, use a preventative diaper rash cream.

We usually use Desitin, but have also had success with A&D Ointment and petroleum jelly. Newborns stool so often that failure to use a preventive cream will quickly result in a tender rash.

Newborn/Sleep

Our children certainly aren't perfect, but they have all been great sleepers. They have regularly slept through the night anywhere from two weeks to three months. Tired parents are often shocked to hear this. Sleep problems are common in children (and therefore parents). Children who sleep well are shown to grow better, behave better and perform better in school. It is essential that children develop good sleep habits. Parents who sleep through the night are happier, fight less, enjoy their children more and make better decisions.

Everything is cuter when you are well rested.

Gordonian Wisdom

Parents should both:
1) wake up and take care of their children in the middle of the night

2) teach the children healthy sleep habits.

Frequently, parents fail to recognize the need to impart good sleep habits to their children. Tired parents wake in the middle of the night and feed their children before assessing their actual need. In doing so, parents inadvertently train their children to feed at night. These parents trade a few hours of sleep one night for a habit of unnecessary night feedings.

Immediately after birth, newborns go through a prolonged awake period lasting several hours. After these precious hours, newborns become extremely sleepy. New parents often report sleepiness interfering with establishing feeding. The average newborn sleeps eighteen hours a day.

 Parents need to wake their newborns every three hours to feed until they are back to birthweight and over 6.5 pounds

Newborns should be awoken and fed every two to three hours at least until their two week check up. Feeding intervals are standardly measured from the start of one feed to the start of the next feed. If your home life is busy, you may consider using a feeding log or timer to help keep this schedule. When parents do need to wake their baby for feedings, unswaddling or changing their newborn's diaper are effective methods to arouse most sleeping babies.

Often, newborns will have nights and days mixed up. Your newborns sleep schedule will begin as it was when they were in the womb. When my wife was pregnant with our first child, her most active time was 10 p.m. As we would settle down for bed, she would start kicking. After her birth, we noted increased alertness and activity at this exact time.

Should you really sleep when the baby is sleeping?

"Sleep when the baby sleeps" is common wisdom passed down to new mothers. This advice greatly frustrated my wife early on. It is simply unrealistic unless you have multiple nannies. My wife recommends choosing some naps to sleep and some to work. Find a balance between sleep and chores.

Count to five before changing your newborn's diapers. With our first, I changed her diaper the minute I heard or smelled any stool. This often resulted in three diaper changes in a ten minute period. She simply wasn't done. Eight children later, I learned to wait a couple minutes and let the baby finish.

Newborn Circumcision Care

In 2009, I started a general pediatric and parenting advice website. Among other newborn topics, I posted a few basic pages on penile adhesions (a common circumcision complication). My website lit up with hits on the topic. Quickly, the Google search "penile adhesions" became the number one way people found my website. It became clear that parents were searching for answers and instructions on circumcision care.

Circumcision remains a hotly debated topic in both medical and non-medical circles. While I recognize the validity of both pro and anti circumcision stances, I do not intend to argue the potential merits of the procedure. My intent in writing this section is to provide an accurate, reliable medical resource to answer questions on post operative circumcision care for newborns.

Types of Circumcisions

The "type" of circumcision refers to the clamp used. There are three major types of circumcision clamps used: Gomco, Plastibell, and Mogen. The method done should be decided by the surgeon.

Newborn boys should only have sponge baths until their umbilical cord and circumcision have healed.

Gomco Most circumcisions in the United States are performed with the Gomco clamp. The name Gomco comes from in the original manufacturer the "Goldstein Manufacturing Company". During a Gomco circumcision, the foreskin is cut off against a metal bell.

Plastibell Worldwide, the Plastibell is the most used circumcision clamp. During a Plastibell circumcision, a plastic ring is inserted into place and then a suture is tied around the ring. In a few days, the ring and the necrotic foreskin falls off. The Plastibell is a disposable item and preferred where instruments cannot be sterilized.

Mogen Mohels (ritual circumcisers) traditionally use Mogen clamps. The name "Mogen" is the Hebrew word for shield. During a Mogen circumcision, the foreskin is pulled through a metal slit, clamped and then cut. In one study, circumcisions done via the Mogen method take less than half the time as the more commonly used clamps. Several recent studies have shown that this reduced procedure time and results in less procedural pain.

As a medical student, I observed and then performed circumcisions with all three types of clamps. I quickly came to prefer the Gomco clamp. The procedure is slower than other types, but seems more controlled and gives better immediate (just after the procedure) results. Long term, all three clamps yield equal results.

The actual circumcision procedure takes only 10 to 15 minutes. While surgical complications can lengthen the time of the procedure, waiting on the proper instruments or medications is the most common cause of delay. Often, children are monitored for 30 minutes after the procedure in the hospital nursery. After the nurses check the surgical site, the baby is returned to his parents.

With each of our boys, I was asked to attend the procedure. This is common courtesy extended to the parents. Some parents have a natural curiosity, or they feel called to be there for their son. Parents who genuinely want to attend the circumcision should. Parents who are unsure or nervous should not attend. Truthfully, most parents help little and serve as a distraction. When parents do attend, I try to explain each step of the procedure and talk mostly to help the parent be more comfortable. While I have not personally had the experience, many pediatricians tell tales of fathers passing out during their son's circumcision. With our sons, I chose not to watch. I feared my presence would be of little help to my son and would only serve to make the doctor and staff nervous.

What should we expect when we first check our son's circumcision?

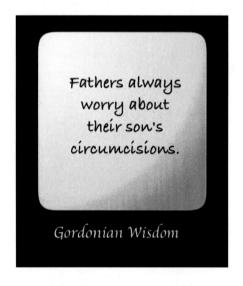

Fathers always worry about their son's circumcisions.

Gordonian Wisdom

Betadine: Betadine is a brown iodine based soap used prior to most surgical procedures. There will often be remnants of this cleanser in the diaper area. Parents often confuse this with dried blood. A damp, warm washcloth should easily clean this up.

Post surgical gauze: Most surgeons leave gauze over the surgical site. This gauze is used to gauge the amount of bleeding after the procedure. There is usually some bleeding, but it should not soak the entire gauze. A 4" x 4" gauze can typically hold two teaspoons of blood. If the gauze is soaked, ask your nurse or doctor to evaluate the surgical site.

Remove the gauze after the first diaper change. While some surgeons recommend repeated application of gauze covered with petroleum jelly, most only recommend application of petroleum jelly. Petroleum jelly is commonly referred to as "Vaseline" (the best known brand name). The petroleum jelly serves several purposes, but early on, it prevents the gauze or diaper from adhering to the surgical site.

What if the gauze gets stuck? Occasionally, the gauze will adhere to the healing circumcised area. This usually happens if the gauze is left in place for a prolonged period of time or the Vaseline was not applied evenly over the surgical site Try soaking the stuck gauze with warm water and then slowly removing the gauze.

Is bleeding normal? Bleeding is the number one immediate post surgical complication. It is not uncommon and it does not mean the surgeon did anything wrong. Sometimes circumcisions just bleed. When circumcisions bleed, they usually bleed in the first couple of hours.

After the initial gauze is removed, there should be very little bleeding. Your son's circumcision is bleeding too much if:

1) you can see blood dripping or
2) there is a quarter sized (or bigger) area of blood on the inside of his diaper or
3) if the whole piece of gauze is soaked.

> # Circumcision complications are rarely the result of the actual circumcision procedure, but more often the result of poor long term care.

If your son's circumcision is bleeding, call your nurse or doctor. It is not an emergency, but it should be addressed urgently. This is not something that can wait hours and is an appropriate reason to go to the emergency room if your doctor's office is closed.

Shortly after birth, all babies should receive a vitamin K injection to aid in clotting. Vitamin K is normally made by an individual's intestinal bacteria. Babies are born without intestinal bacteria and, therefore, without vitamin K. Extremely rarely, parents refuse vitamin K.

These vitamin K deficient newborns are at risk for excessive bleeding. Infants who do not receive vitamin K should not be circumcised in the hospital.

It is Jewish custom to perform circumcision on the eighth day of life. As with many religious traditions, there is a good medical reason. We now know that an individual's natural clotting ability peaks on day eight.

Early in my pediatric career, one of my then pregnant families asked me to circumcise their son during his Bris. The Bris needed to occur on their son's eighth day of life and their family and rabbi would attend. A little nervous, I agreed. It seemed with more people watching, something would surely go wrong. On his eighth day of life, I opened our office early for the event. The infant, his parents, their rabbi, six more members of their family, my nurse and I crowded into one of our procedure rooms. Despite twelve people crammed into a small room, it was amazingly quiet. As I proceed with the circumcision, the silence was only broken by the rabbi saying prayers. The newborn boy did fabulously! He never cried, and there were no complications.

How do doctors treat persistent circumcision bleeding?

Epinephrine and Surgicel® are commonly employed to stop post circumcision bleeding. Epinephrine may be dripped onto the bleeding area. Surgicel® is a medicated gauze that aids clotting. When Surgicel® is applied, it is left on to become part of the clot. After application, Surgicel® turns a dark gray/black color. If your son had Surgicel® applied, leave it alone and it will fall off on its own.

Is swelling common? Circumcisions look best immediately after removal of the clamp. In only a few minutes, swelling begins. The swelling occurs at the edge of the remaining foreskin. It will resolve in one to two weeks.

Circumcision Pain

Pain management should begin prior to the procedure. EMLA cream and lidocaine are the most commonly accepted medications used for circumcision operative anesthesia.

EMLA EMLA is an anesthetic cream approved by the FDA in 1998. EMLA stands for Eutectic Mixture of Local Anesthetics. EMLA is often used to help minimize procedural pain for circumcisions and other procedures. Most research shows few to no side effects with EMLA. To obtain maximal effect, EMLA should be applied 60 to 90 minutes prior to the procedure. EMLA is shown to be effective in reducing circumcision procedural pain, but it is not as effective as injected lidocaine.

My oldest son was born and, therefore, circumcised during my residency at the Children's Hospital of Alabama. Maggie's OB performed the circumcision as was tradition in the Birmingham area. I was in my pediatric training and knew enough about EMLA to request it for my son. Our OB was unfamiliar with EMLA and, like most doctors in the 1990s, did not routinely use any anesthetic for circumcisions. Maggie's OB was awesome. He ordered the EMLA and then patiently sat in the newborn nursery waiting for it to take effect before beginning surgery.

Injected lidocaine Injected lidocaine is the most effective way to prevent circumcision surgical pain. Lidocaine without epinephrine should be used. Lidocaine is often used before doctors place sutures (stitches). Lidocaine is injected at the base of the penis, just prior to beginning the procedure. Lidocaine begins to work in three to five minutes and lasts 30 to 120 minutes.

Tylenol Some practitioners recommend Tylenol (acetaminophen) for pain control. I do not. Tylenol can control pain, but it will also mask fever. Accurate knowledge of an infant's temperature is critical for proper medical management. Febrile infants require further medical work-up and additional days of hospital care.

Swaddling It is important for the infant to be fully restrained during the circumcision. The circumcision boards are designed with disposable straps to effectively restrain the newborn. Unfortunately, this spread out position is uncomfortable for newborns. Newborns are happiest when swaddled snugly and warmly. Swaddling an infant's arms near his mouth during the circumcision procedure is also shown to help alleviate pain.

Pacifiers and Sucrose Pacifiers dipped in sucrose also aid in pain control. Multiple research studies have examined the analgesic effect of a variety of sweet tasting solutions. Of these, sucrose (aka table sugar) seems the most effective. In addition, sucrose delivered via a pacifier further improves pain control.

What should be done in the immediate post-operative time period?

Most boys are calm and swaddled upon presentation to their parents. Upon arrival, parents should hold and comfort their son. Often, boys will need to be fed at this time. There is no need to rush and check the circumcision if the nurse just evaluated the area. Check the diaper area in 30 to 60 minutes or when he needs a diaper change.

After our boys were circumcised, they were fussy the rest of the day. They were consoled by swaddling, a pacifier and nursing. Diaper changes are important to monitor the surgical site for complications and to apply petroleum jelly, but they do seem to cause discomfort.

How to apply petroleum jelly (Vaseline) While most parents are instructed to apply petroleum jelly to the tender area of the penis, I prefer a different method. Applying Vaseline directly to the diaper causes less pain and is much easier. Position the diaper in place, fold the diaper to determine where the Vaseline is needed and then apply liberally. Vaseline prevents the head of the penis from healing (sticking) to the diaper and helps prevent infection.

When do we start to retract the foreskin? There is no need for retraction in the immediate post operative period. The infant's penis is too tender for manipulation and retraction may cause bleeding.

Good care in the immediate post operative period

1) Monitor for bleeding
2) Expect swelling/ redness

3) Swaddle, feed and pacifier for pain control
4) Apply petroleum jelly to the surgical area
5) No retraction (yet)

The Healing Phase
(The first two weeks)

Circumcision healing can take up
to two weeks. During this time,
close monitoring and proper care
aid the healing process.

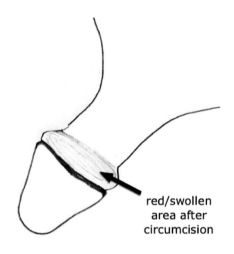

red/swollen
area after
circumcision

Swelling and Bruising Post circumcision swelling typically occurs on the cut edge of the foreskin. The swelling that developed in the first several hours
usually takes several days to a
couple weeks to resolve. Once
the swelling has resolved, most
circumcisions have completely
healed.

Post circumcision bruising usually occurs at the base of the penis. Bruising is most often the result of injected lidocaine. The bruising heals
quickly and is often resolved after a week.

Yellow Scabs A scab on the penile head appears unlike healing elsewhere
on the body. These areas of healing often look yellowish and soft. Prior to
circumcision, most boys have penile adhesions (skin bridges) between the
end of the foreskin and the penile head. These natural adhesions prevent
full foreskin retraction. To circumcise an individual, these bridges must
be broken. The process of breaking these bonds often leaves small abrasions on the penile head. As these abrasions heal, yellow scabs form.
Some boys have multiple adhesions and therefore multiple scabs. These
scabs heal slowly over the first week.

Infection Circumcision, like any procedure that involves a needle or scal-
pel, carries a risk of infection. The use of betadine soap and sterile in-

struments should minimize this risk. Fortunately, infection is a rare complication of circumcision. I have seen one infected circumcision in my first fifteen years of practice.

Plastibell During Plastibell circumcisions, a plastic ring is inserted into place and then a suture is tied around the ring. The plastic ring should fall off on its own between days five to eight.

What should we do during the healing phase?

Apply Petroleum Jelly Petroleum jelly should be applied with every diaper change until the circumcision is completely healed. Petroleum jelly post circumcision serves two purposes: it helps reduce the risk of infections and reduce the risk of the cut edge healing to the diaper. Petroleum jelly is typically needed during the first week after circumcision. Apply petroleum jelly with every diaper change. While you can place the petroleum jelly on the tender penile head, as previously stated, it is easier to place it directly on the diaper.

No Warm Water While researching this book, I found several websites that recommend washing the surgical area multiple times each day with warm water and sometimes soap during the healing phase. I can find no medical research supporting this recommendation. Many physicians recommend warm water to loosen stuck gauze. I doubt warm water would cause serious problems, but it seems an unnecessary discomfort.

No Retraction (yet) For the majority of newborns, there is no need for foreskin retraction at this time. Regular retraction becomes important only when the foreskin rests on the head of the penis.

Most new parents have heard other parents stories of "re-circumcision" or "the doctor didn't do a good job on his circumcision." These complications are rarely the result of the actual circumcision procedure, but more often the result of poor long term care. Unfortunately, many parents and many doctors are unfamiliar with proper long-term care. Most often, the doctor who circumcises a newborn is not the doctor providing long-term care. Instruction on circumcision care is an important part of preventative care and should begin at two weeks. (see pages 54-55)

Fever (Birth to Three Months)

Fever in the first three months of life is an emergency. During this time, a rectal temperature of 100.4°F or higher should trigger an immediate medical visit. It is difficult to distinguish between a 1-month-old with a minor viral illness (a "cold") and one with a severe infection like meningitis. An adult with meningitis will look very sick and report fever, stiff neck and a severe headache. In contrast, an infant with meningitis will present only with fever and fussiness.

Your children will always be their sickest when your spouse is out of town.

Gordonian Wisdom

While research and clinical practice varies, most children less than two months old with a single temperature of 100.4°F or higher should have a lumbar puncture (spinal tap) with culture, CBC, blood culture and catheterized urine culture. Often, these children will require hospitalization or injected antibiotics while awaiting the culture results.

Minimize the number of visitors to your home. All visitors must be healthy. Don't believe "it's just allergies" or "my doctor says I'm not contagious." Make sure that all visitors wash their hands before touching your newborn.

Parents of newborns should isolate them. Newborns should not be out in public. Do not take your child to restaurants, grocery stores, the mall or theme parks. And yes, once I hospitalized a febrile 6-day-old who went to Disney World with relatives visiting from Ohio. If you *must* go to the store, minimize your baby's exposure. Go on a Tuesday morning when stores are not busy. Keep him covered. Do not let strangers hold or even touch him. Minimal exposure does not mean you need to stay inside for two months. Visiting friends or going for a walk should be safe, minimal exposure activities.

After our fifth child was born, we choose to attend our church's 7 a.m. Sunday service in an attempt to avoid crowds. Each week, the church was sparsely filled with elderly adults, either by themselves or as a couple. Maggie and I were clearly the youngest adults and there were no other children. Many heads turned to stare as we entered (I'm sure we were not perfectly quiet). Now, our church, like many in Florida, tends to be causal - especially the early or later services. Some people attend in shorts or even a t-shirt. The 7 a.m. service was freezing cold as the air conditioning was geared for the packed later services. After the first week, our older boys (then five and seven years old) decided to stay warm, so they wore a coat and tie. For two months, Maggie and I marched our semi-formally dressed children and baby into a 7 a.m. church service full of staring, elderly adults.

Two Weeks

Maggie and I have attempted to provide the "gift of music" for our children. We own two guitars, half a dozen violins and a piano. Three of our children take piano lessons. We are blessed with a high energy piano teacher who comes to our home. Piano lessons often end with a full on jam session.

It is on "piano nights" that I am reminded just how great our younger children sleep. While children #3, #4 and #5 bang on our piano, Maggie and I are putting the younger children to bed. Our youngest three share the room right next to the piano.

The first night your new baby sleeps through the night, one of your other kids will wake you up.

Gordonian Wisdom

Despite the piano, we proceed with our regular bedtime routine. Our children do not question their bedtime routine, as it is a consistent part of their lives. At the end of the routine, we read books, say prayers and kiss them goodnight. On "piano nights" (just like other nights) they settle down and are asleep within 5 to 15 minutes. In our home, our good sleep habits are essential and we believe they begin at two weeks.

Two Weeks Sleep

When can we let our baby sleep all night?

Parents should stop night wakings when healthy babies:

1) weigh at least 6.5 pounds 2) are back to their birth weight by two weeks. Two-week-olds will not sleep all night, but hopefully you will get longer sleeping stretches. During the day, wake your son every three hours to feed. This is an important part of creating a stimulating daytime. At night, let your healthy 2-week-old sleep.

> **While it is your responsibility to wake up and feed your newborn, it is likewise your responsibility to teach him to sleep.**

The Overall Sleep Plan

I recognize that there are whole books on teaching children to sleep written by doctors who have researched sleep for their entire careers. Fortunately, these books are rarely needed and should be reserved for the small percentage of children who need them. The vast majority of children will learn healthy sleep habits without the need for drastic measures.

The process of teaching a child good sleep habits can be broken down into three basic steps:

1) creating the right environment for sleep
2) spacing out feedings
3) teaching children to fall asleep on their own.

Ideally, you are reading this book holding a newborn. The process of teaching your child to sleep all night often seems effortless when initiated from the beginning. Most children learn to sleep all night after the first step. In some children, the other steps are needed to retain these good sleep habits.

Creating the Right Environment for Sleep (Step 1)

How do we begin teaching our newborn to sleep?

Teaching your baby to sleep should begin shortly after birth. Begin by creating a loud, bright, stimulating daytime where people talk at full voice, listen to music and run the vacuum. Yes, even during naps. Do not create a library-like environment at home. Stop shushing your family and friends. Children raised in artificially quiet environments seem unable to adapt to new, less ideal environments (travel, visitors and college). In contrast, nighttime should be dark and boring, where one parent wakes and calmly feeds the newborn in dim lighting. Do not turn on the over-head lights at night, unless absolutely necessary. Use night lights or lamps to create a distinctly different nighttime environment. Minimize eye contact. Save all the "you're the cutest baby in the world" talk for the daytime.

Create the right home environment to encourage your child to sleep at night.

All too often, I find dedicated new parents who both wake at 2 a.m. to feed their bundle of joy. Mom nurses the baby, while dad sings songs and catches up on World Cup Soccer scores. Given the flurry of activity, the child is unable to distinguish the difference between 2 a.m. and 2 p.m. These new parents are wasting valuable energy and giving their child the wrong message.

At night, only one parent should wake up. Children should be fed with an "eat and go back to bed" mentality. If your child is awake, alert and calm at night put him in his bed. If he is fussy and needs to be held, hold him and love him. Realistically, it will take weeks before a properly trained newborn begins to differentiate night verses day.

Not surprisingly, our earliest sleeper was our eighth. She was consistently sleeping six hours stretches prior to two weeks. With seven older siblings constantly wanting her attention, our dog barking, a rooster crowing in our backyard and piano or violin practice during the day, she quickly figured out that nighttime was meant for sleep.

Forget lost socks, where do the pacifiers go?

Gordonian Wisdom

Beginning a Bedtime Routine - Creating a Habit

Begin a regular bedtime routine after the two-week check up. A bedtime routine will help signify the end of day and beginning of nighttime. Your child is ready for a bedtime routine once:

1) he is back to his birthweight
2) his umbilical area and circumcision have healed.

 Establish a set bedtime routine.

While you can begin a bedtime at any time, I recommend you plan to finish the entire routine around 10 p.m. An eight hour sleep stretch is a reasonable goal in the first couple of months. A 10 p.m. to 6 a.m. should feel like all night. But a 7 p.m. to 3 a.m. stretch just doesn't feel as good. When starting a bedtime routine, work with your infant. If he seems tired and ready to feed at 8 p.m., then work with it. Use 8 p.m. as a starting point. Bedtime can always be adjusted.

Our newborn bedtime routine:
1) Feed/burp
2) Bathe
3) Dress/swaddle
4) Feed again (top off)/burp
5) Pacifier and place in crib.

As you begin the nighttime routine, dim the lights and speak calmly. Bottle feed or nurse your child a full feeding. For newborns, a full feeding usually takes 40 minutes. After this initial feeding, burp your infant. While burping, draw a warm bath. Draw the bath so that your baby can hear the water running in the tub. Eventually, this will become an audible cue helping signal it's time for sleep. Calmly bathe your child. Often, newborns initially dislike taking baths. Given time, he will begin to enjoy his evening bath. After the bath, dress your infant in a fresh diaper and pajamas. Swaddle your baby. Breast or bottle feed a little more to "top him off." This feeding should only last about five minutes. Give your baby a pacifier and place him in his bed. Be consistent and your infant will respond. After only a few nights of this routine, you will see your child relax and prepare for sleep. Ideally, your infant will be placed in bed awake but drowsy. It is OK early on if your infant is placed in bed asleep. If possible, place your child in his bed groggy, but still awake. Eventually, your child must learn how to fall asleep on his own.

A Few Notes on Swaddling

Prior to the "Back to Sleep" program in the 1990s, most United States infants slept on their tummies (prone). I know my parents placed me on my stomach for sleep. At the time, experts thought that prone sleeping was safer as it protected infants from choking if they spit up. Parents did not question this advice, as prone sleeping infants sleep better. Unfortunately, children placed prone to sleep are at a much higher risk for SIDS (Sudden Infant Death Syndrome). The "Back to Sleep" program was launched to encourage back (supine) sleeping. Consequently, the United States has seen a dramatic reduction in the rate of SIDS.

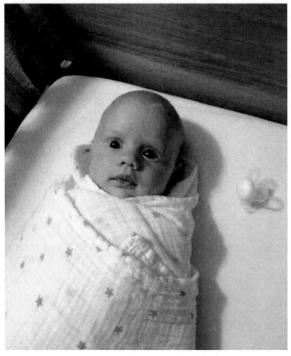

As a medical student in the late 1990s, our professors taught us the merits of supine sleep. Our job was to educate new parents. This was not easy. Parents easily understood the theoretical advantage of lowering the risk of SIDS, but their children did not sleep as well. Children placed on their backs did not settle down as easily, or sleep as well. Pediatricians and parents quickly adopted swaddling to comfort these children when placed on their backs for sleep.

I learned to swaddle thanks to a militant nurse during my medical school newborn nursery rotation. She insisted that we re-swaddle each newborn after we examined them. We all shared a healthy fear of this nurse and consequently learned to swaddle as well as a group of 24-year-olds could.

As the popularity of swaddling has increased, so have concerns about its practice. Some experts believe that swaddling could increase the risk of

SIDS and increase a child's risk of hip problems. Swaddling SIDS concerns relate to older children. I will discuss these later. In the first two months of life, swaddling clearly reduces crying and reduces the risk of SIDS.

Swaddling techniques and practices vary by culture. Swaddling techniques that strap an infant to a rigid board are shown to increase an individual's risk of developmental dysplasia of the hips (DDH). The Navajo Indian "cradle board" and the Japanese "swathing diaper" are notorious for causing DDH and do not allow the baby to flex his hips. Modern American swaddling techniques are not proven to increase the risk of DDH. There is, however, enough evidence to be concerned. Children should be swaddled in a manner that allows maximal flexion of their hips.

After reviewing the data on swaddling, I have come to embrace "hip flexed" swaddling. This is best accomplished with the swaddling technique where the last fold is up. In this technique, the arms are folded in, and in the final (up from the bottom) fold the hips are flexed. See step-by-step swaddling instructions on following pages. Safe swaddling allows for flexion of the hips, uses a flexible blanket and should be snug but not tight.

How to Safely Swaddle Your Infant

Step 1: Place your infant on a rectangular blanket with his shoulders even with the top edge of the blanket.	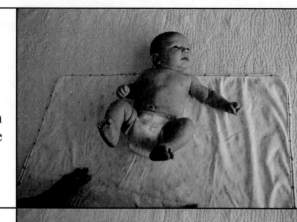
Step 2: While holding his hands together and down with your right hand, fold the left corner across your baby's left shoulder.	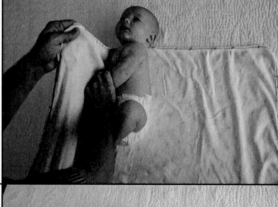
Step 3: Roll your baby on his side and tuck the left corner of the blanket behind the child's shoulder.	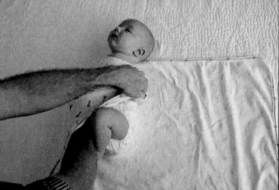

Step 4:
Fold the right corner of the blanket across your baby's left shoulder.

Step 5:
Tuck the right corner of the blanket behind the child's shoulder.

Step 6:
Fold the bottom flap up and wrap the flaps around the infant's back.

Final Result:
A snug swaddle and a happy baby with free hip movement.

Gregory Gordon, MD

Waking up between Two Weeks and Two Months

Parent Question:

Our daughter is healthy and was back to her birth weight at her two week check up. What should I do when my daughter wakes in the middle of the night between two weeks and two months?

Remember, nighttime should be dark and boring. When your daughter wakes in the middle of the night, do as little as you can to calm her down and get her back to sleep. If you think she may settle back down without being picked up, try giving her a pacifier or tightening up her swaddle. Minimize eye contact and avoid talking to her.

If she is crying to the point where you need to pick her up, check her diaper (and change if needed), give her a pacifier, re-swaddle, walk and bounce, or offer calming words. If you are unable to soothe her and she is due to be fed, then it is OK to feed her. If you must feed her, make sure she gets a full feeding. In our home, we try to end all night feedings by two months old.

Six Week Old Waking

Parent Question:

Our 6-week-old has been sleeping in a bassinet in our room and he's waking every two hours to feed. We're wondering if he's just pacifying himself and does this mean that we should consider moving him to his crib in his own room (in other words, is Mom's proximity slowing him from stretching out his night feedings)?

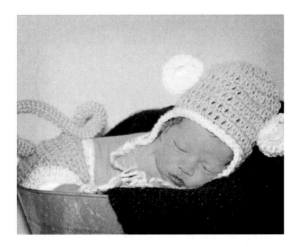

Newborns often need to feed every two to three hours. That said, many newborns will also pacify on their mother's breast for comfort. Is he nursing with effort and interest? Have you ever offered him a pacifier first? You need to make sure he is fully awake. During the night, if he is not completely awake (or you are unsure), offer him a pacifier first. Once you have decided to feed him, make sure he stays awake long enough for a full feeding. Stimulate him halfway through his feeding: changing his diaper, rubbing his back or undressing him.

There is a connection beyond normal senses between mothers and babies. Both mother and baby often sleep better in separate rooms. I think, however, it is too early to move him to another room. If you move him now, you will be doing a lot of walking in the middle of the night.

At six weeks:
1) keep the day bright and stimulating
2) maintain a consistent bedtime routine
3) stimulate for full feeding
4) try a pacifier first when you don't think he needs to feed
     and soon he (and you) will be sleeping well.

Maggie feels babies indicate readiness to sleep through the night when they stop having dirty diapers at night

Temperature in Room

Parent Question:

What is the normal room temperature we should keep in our 5-week-old's nursery? We usually keep it about 73°F but many books/websites say to keep the house in the 60s. That seems too cool. We don't want to over-heat him because we swaddle him at night but we don't want him too cold either.

Keep your home at a temperature where you as parents are comfortable - 73°F is fine. I would dress your baby a little warmer than you and swaddle him in a blanket. A 1-month-old is old enough to let you know (through crying) if he is uncomfortable. As for "the experts" who recommend 60°F, I'd bet they either sell air conditioning systems or are referring to heating the home up to the high 60s.

Do you recommend co-sleeping?

I do not recommend co-sleeping. I do agree that when humans slept in caves, newborns slept with or on top of their mothers. I also recognize that babies sleep their best on their mother's belly.

The American Academy of Pediatrics does not recommend co-sleeping either. The AAP cites the small number of children who are crushed and suffocated each year in the United States as a primary reason.

> With first children, we parents make mistakes because we try too hard. With second children, parents never make the same mistakes - we make different ones.
>
> *Gordonian Wisdom*

My main objection to co-sleeping is failure to see it work. Co-sleeping has to end sometime. Your child cannot still be sleeping with his mother when he is 14 years old. So, somewhere between birth and 14 years old, co-sleeping must end. The transition to his own bed gets increasingly difficult as the months and years go by.

When is it easiest to end a bad habit? Consider an example of a child holding a pencil incorrectly. If he begins holding it incorrectly the first time, and it is not corrected, he will continue to improperly use it. Attempting to correct the issue later on only presents new challenges and a hard-to-break habit. As with anything, it is best to avoid bad habits from the start.

One of the families in my practice came to me frustrated with the baby's grandparents. The grandparents had recently decided that they could no longer baby sit their grandson overnight or in the evenings. The parents had been co-sleeping with their 8-month-old son. He had always co-slept well for his parents. The grandparents, though eager to help, had been unable to sleep or get their grandson to sleep while the parents had been away.

Co-sleeping was dividing the family. The parents were frustrated with the grandparents. The grandparents (who wanted to help) were exhausted and frustrated with the parents. After a long discussion with the family and several weeks of hard, emotional work, their son finally learned good sleep habits.

> **In the middle of the night, you will be tempted by short cuts that will create bad sleep habits long term.**

Fortunately, this family recognized the problem and corrected it. Too often, parents do not see this as a problem, or worse, when one parent wants to co-sleep and the other does not. I have found several families where mother and child sleep together and the father sleeps in the guest room. This ultimately damages the couple's relationship and eventually their family.

Parenting begins with a newborn that is completely dependent. Good parenting should create a self-sufficient, independent person. We parents need to let our kids "grow up." We need to teach our children to do tasks and then back off. Teach your son to dress himself, and then let him dress himself. Teach your daughter how to feed herself, and then let her feed herself. Teach your baby how to sleep and let him sleep.

The easiest way to impart good sleep habits to your child is to develop these habits from the beginning. By co-sleeping, even for a few months, you miss the best, most natural opportunity to give you child the gift of good sleep.

Define Sleeping Through the Night.

Sleeping through the night in the first four months of life is sleeping six to eight hours consistently at night without any feedings. I realize that, to many expecting parents, this is not their personal definition. Trust me, there will come a time that a six hour stretch is relished.

This initial definition is simply a starting point. A consistent six to eight hour stretch means that your child "gets it." They understand that night is for sleep. As your child grows and becomes more physically active, these stretches will slowly increase.

Only Wants Mommy

Parent Question:

My daughter is almost nine weeks old. When she fights sleep, she will not calm herself and refuses to let anyone else calm her down but me. This happens both at night and during the day. I have tried leaving the house for a few minutes to see if she will allow someone else to calm her if I am not around, but I always return to her screaming. We are at a complete loss and refuse to let her cry it out at this age. My husband and I want to go out, but we are afraid to leave her with a babysitter-especially in the evening when this seems to happen the most. What should we do? I should add that I am exclusively breastfeeding, but she does not fall asleep while feeding. She will also allow someone (even me) to feed her a bottle, so I don't think this is tied to hunger or comfort from breastfeeding.

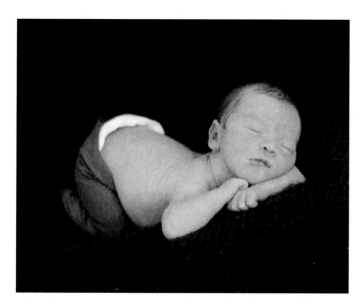

Children often prefer their mother. More than once, a Gordon child with a skinned knee has run past me to seek the comfort only a mother can provide. My medical degree and years of pediatric medical experience seemed to mean little to a child with a bleeding knee. Our children younger than two typically prefer their mom.

When she cries, do you typically have to nurse her to calm her down? If you do, then you are training her to calm down through nursing, and therefore, only you would be able to calm her down. In general, if you have completed a strict bedtime routine and she is waking shortly after being placed in her bed, then try to do as little as possible. Try giving her a pacifier, swaddling, hold and bounce her. These things could be repeated by her father or a babysitter.

At her age, it is not wrong to nurse her to sleep and transfer her to her bed. It is best not to, however, as this eventually leads to nighttime waking beyond six months. I also agree she is too young to try crying it out.

Sometimes, as fathers, we need to be forced to step up. Typically, fathers defer to mothers when it comes to crying infants. When forced to take care and console our little ones, we can. One of my 9-month-olds and I bonded only after a family emergency forced us to spend a weekend camping without his mother. Try leaving your husband in charge for an evening as a first step. Given time, this will get better.

Follow up / Parent Response

Our routine had been for daddy to put our 3-year-old to sleep while I put our daughter to bed, but we reversed roles after reading your advice. This seems to have done the trick. I also have started pumping a bottle for her to have right before bedtime so she is not relying on me alone. She is three months old now, and her daddy puts her to sleep most nights without an issue. He is still rocking her, but we are slowly transitioning to laying her down in her bed awake. Thanks so much for your help!

Crying after Bedtime Routine

Parent Question:

My 4-week-old daughter frequently cries after her bedtime routine. Her crying does not last long - only about one minute. Should I just let her cry, or is this harming her? She slept six hours the last few nights, so I don't really want to change anything.

Children often cry when placed in their beds. If her crying only lasts a minute or two and is "half-hearted," then just let her cry. It seems it is part of her settling down routine. I am impressed that you are already working on placing her in her bed awake. This should help her become a great sleeper. However, she is young enough that it is OK to pick her up and then transfer her to her bed asleep.

2- month-old Not Sleeping – Getting Close

Parent Question:

I am having a very difficult time getting my 2-month-old daughter to sleep past 3 a.m. I changed her bed time from 8 p.m. to 10 p.m. in hopes it would improve things, but it hasn't. During the daytime, she typically gets two to three naps for a total of five to six hours. Our nighttime routine consists of a bath, a feeding and being rocked to sleep. I keep the light dim, usually just a nightlight. She has just started to be able to self settle, but not consistently. I have no problem putting her down for the night. She typically wakes at around 2 a.m. for a feeding and easily goes back to sleep. However, she wakes up shortly thereafter, around 3:30 a.m. I often struggle the rest of the night trying to put her to sleep unsuccessfully. I may be able to put her to sleep, but she always wakes within 20 to 30 minutes. Finally, I give in at 6 a.m. and bring her to my bed to sleep with me (in which she sleeps for another three hours). I really don't like co-sleeping and would prefer not to depend on it. Do you have any suggestions that might help (as well as things I might be doing to further aggravate the situation)?

Overall, it sounds like you are doing everything right. I am pleased to hear that your 2-month-old is already sleeping four to six hour stretches at night and seems to understand that night is for sleeping. The goal I set for my patients is consistently sleeping six to eight hours by four months. I realize this may not seem like success to a mother getting six hours of sleep a night. However, it is my experience that children who reach this goal by four months gradually increase their hours of nighttime sleep as they grow and become more physically active.

If she is a well-grown, healthy child, I would recommend you gradually space out her daytime feedings closer to every 3.5 to 4 hours. If your baby is a frequent feeder, slowly space out her feedings by increasing the minimum interval by fifteen minutes at a time. For more information, see spacing out feedings on page 67.

If you have not already tried, I would recommend you try a pacifier and swaddling to help settle her down at night. My 2-month-olds typically liked to have their legs swaddled and their arms free. I agree with your stance on co-sleeping. While it is easy in the short run, it makes sleep more difficult in the long haul.

Bottom line: It sounds like you are doing all the right things, and she is close to sleeping well. Hang in there!

Two Weeks Feeding

Supplementing or Starting a Bottle

Parent Question:

I have an 8-week-old baby who has only been fed breast milk thus far. I plan to return to work in four weeks and I will be stopping breastfeeding completely. I want to slowly introduce formula over the next couple of weeks to make the transition easier and hopefully find the right formula. How should I slowly introduce formula over the next couple of weeks and what type of formula should I begin with?

The cessation of breastfeeding can be a sensitive subject. Realize that you do not have to stop breastfeeding when you return to work. Some women are able to nurse in the evenings and weekends. My guess is you are aware of this option and have decided to stop nursing for other reasons.

I would recommend you introduce bottles as soon as possible (even if they contain breast milk). It is best to wean down slowly from breastfeeding as it will be easiest on mother and baby. I would recommend starting with a milk based formula. Some breastfed infants refuse to take bottles as it is different than nursing. If your baby is already able to take a bottle, this transition should go smoothly.

Breastfeeding parents should periodically bottle feed their babies, after breastfeeding has been well established, usually around two to three weeks.

When our fourth child was four months old, Maggie and I attempted to go on a date. Our baby was healthy and had been nursing well. We left her with a full bottle of pumped breast milk and an experienced, trusted baby-sitter. Halfway through dinner, our babysitter called. Our daughter was refusing to take the bottle and crying inconsolably. After cutting our date short, I, the "expert," also failed repeatedly to feed her a bottle. She would only calm down by nursing. She had not learned to take a bottle when she was younger. We never were able to teach her to take a bottle. During the next few months, our dates were limited to only a couple of hours. It is this experience that led me to encourage breastfeeding mothers to periodically bottle feed starting around two weeks.

Changing Formulas after Problems

Many problems are attributed to formula preparations including: gas, fussiness, spitting up, bloody stools and constipation.

Most experts would agree, your baby needs to try a new formula if they have both fussiness and bloody stools. After that it gets more complicated.

Gas is rarely caused by the formula. Gas is more often caused by poor feeding technique, inadequate burping or the unintentional feeding of air bubbles. Make sure the bottle is tilted enough to keep the nipple full of formula. Do not shake up a bottle then immediately feed it to a baby. Allow the bottle to settle before the feeding. Try new bottle types (designed for gas) or nipples if your baby remains gassy.

Fussiness could be a formula problem or it could be attributed to a myriad of other problems - including but not limited to: underfeeding, overfeeding, reflux (GERD), normal infant fussiness, thrush, or inadequate burping.

Spitting up is normal for babies. An added rice starch formula may help some, but severe cases of reflux may need medication. See the section on GERD (page 51) and the section on rice (page 86).

Occasionally, I will recommend elemental formulas to help treat constipation. This use takes advantage of the most common side effect of elemental formulas - diarrhea. Many children need only a small percentage (blended in) or even a single bottle a day of an elemental formula to address their constipation issues.

When making formula changes, it makes the most sense to try different types of formulas. If your child is fussy on a cow's milk protein based formula, do not try another cow's milk based formula. It makes more sense to try soy, lactose-free or elemental formula next.

When formula changes are made, hopeful parents often believe them to help initially. Children seem less gassy and happier. Wait two weeks before considering a formula change a success. Some healthcare providers take advantage of the phenomena and just keep randomly changing formula's every time a parent complains. When changing formulas, the question is not "will it help" but "will it continue to help beyond the first week?"

Increasing a Baby's Feedings

Parent Question:

My son is one month old and I have a question about feeding. I have been feeding him 3 to 3.5 ounces so far (from pumping or the occasional formula supplement). Should I continue that amount or bump it up? I haven't really seen many suggestions on this. When I breastfeed him, I just watch his cues to see that he is eating enough. I want to make sure, how-

ever, I'm not over or under feeding him. He is up to par with the "output," so I think he is doing OK. I just want to make sure.

Feeding your baby an appropriate amount of milk is clearly a balance. Many parents feel like they are in the dark as it hard to know how much. The "right" amount is different for every child. Your child's growth (especially weight) is the best indicator. Your healthcare provider should give you feedback at well check ups.

In between health visits, continue to monitor your baby at home. I agree that monitoring urine and stool output is helpful. Most one month old children will be fussy if they are underfed or overfed. Typically, overfed infants will spit up more than usual. Three-and-a-half ounces sounds like a great feeding. If he periodically seems like he wants more, you should try a little more. Page 19 shows a table of average daily milk consumption that may give you some guidelines. If you are concerned or just want peace of mind, make an appointment with your healthcare provider.

Two Weeks Fussiness

Few things make me cringe more than when new parents say, "She's a really good baby. She hardly ever cries." These always seem to be the parents that are back in my office three weeks later begging for help with their fussy, crying baby. It is extremely rare to have a fussy crying 2-week-old. As babies age, they tend to cry more. The average baby cries their most at six weeks. This "normal" crying is at its worst in the evening.

The typical story for the stay-at-home mother and the father with a day job goes like this: The mother has the day she dreamt about where her infant child reaches up touches her face and smiles for the first time. About an hour before the father arrives home the baby begins to cry. When the new father walks in the door, the baby is crying, the mother is crying, dinner is burning in the oven, and the phone is ringing (it's his mother

Fussy babies never cry at doctors appointments.

Gordonian Wisdom

calling to check on the baby). He then says, "Why did we ever have this baby?" The mother cries more because she really had a great day.

Crying is the main way young children express their needs. Crying can be a sign of a routine daily need or a life threatening illness. Most often, infants cry when they are hungry, tired, cold or need a diaper change. With time, parents often learn their child's varied cries. Most parents can tell the difference between a fussy, tired cry and a cry of pain. Sometimes, crying is rooted in illness. Persistent coughing, thrush, teething and even meningitis can be a cause of crying.

Research demonstrates that infants learn to cry to get their parents' attention. Their cries are trained to bother their parents. Often, friends ask me, "How do you handle eight children at home and then go to work and deal with more crying children?" The answer is simple. I am not nearly as disturbed by the crying, screaming and tantrums at work. It is much more difficult to be a stay-at-home parent. Persistent crying is very frustrating as a parent. It leads the best, experienced parents to question their actions. "What am I missing?" "What is wrong with this child?"

Colic is the worst of crying. Colic is defined as more than three hours of unexplained crying, at least three days per week in a healthy, well-grown child. It is every parent's nightmare. I was a colicky baby. My parents tell stories of arriving home from a date to find both the baby and babysitter crying. Fortunately, colic is rare. I probably only see two or three cases of unexplained crying each year. More often, fussiness is the result of milk intolerances or GERD. Colic is a diagnosis of exclusion - meaning it can only be diagnosed once all other causes have been ruled out.

Fussy 2-week-old

Parent Question:

Our 2-week-old son was so fussy last week that we took him to a walk-in clinic. In less than ten minutes, the doctor diagnosed him with colic. How does he know my son has colic? What do you

recommend for colic?

I'd first recommend seeing a real doctor! Colic cannot be diagnosed in a single office visit. Colic is a diagnosis of exclusion, meaning a child can only be diagnosed with colic once all other reasonable diagnoses have been excluded. Colic is a true entity recognized across the world in multiple cultures. The cause is unknown. The name "colic" comes from the belief that the pain originates in the colon. Typical cases of colic begin at three to four weeks and last until three to four months. Colic is defined as more than three hours of unexplained crying per day. Despite their fussiness, children with colic grow well.

I see fussy babies every day in my practice and only rarely do I diagnose colic. Is your son growing appropriately? Underfeeding and overfeeding are major causes of infant fussiness. Children should regain their birthweight by two weeks old and then gain 0.5 to 1.0 ounces at day (fifteen to 30 grams). Formula or milk intolerance is also a common cause of fussiness at your son's age. Is he formula fed? If he is breastfed, have you tried restricting cow's milk in your diet? The most common treatable cause of infant fussiness is spitting up or gastroesphogeal reflux (GERD).

This case has me really fired up. You need to take him to his regular primary care doctor to be evaluated. Colic should not be a diagnosis on a single ten-minute visit. Good luck and let me know how he does.

Spitting up (GERD)

When I was a pediatric intern, my wife and I proudly took our first child to the Department of Pediatrics holiday party. After parking, my wife nursed our daughter so she would not be hungry during the event. Not too many young doctors are brave (or stupid) enough to have a child during their internship. Medical interns are known to work a ridiculous number of hours. Many of my memories of that year are clouded by fatigue. However, I vividly remember watching my daughter's spit up soak the suit pants of a prominent pediatric cardiologist at that holiday party.

All babies spit up, but few need medical treatment. It is important to differentiate "normal" spitting up from GERD (gastroesophageal reflux disease). Normal spitting is non-projectile vomiting of white to yellowish, often curdled milk in a happy child who continues to grow well. This spit up often looks like a large amount and may soak the baby and his parent. Projectile vomiting, on the other hand, sprays out with force and can be a sign of a more severe problem.

GERD is the extreme form of spitting up. Spitting up becomes a medical problem when it affects an individual's growth or causes pain.

Parents often report their child "spits up everything he eats." While it may look like this to the concerned parent, most babies only spit up a fraction of their milk. Try pouring a few ounces of milk on your floor or a burp cloth. You will quickly see that the amount of spit up is not the full feeding. If the child continues to grow well, I am not concerned about the reported volume of spit up. In my pediatric practice, I have yet to see a child who spit up so much he did not gain weight.

The more common treatable concern with GERD is fussiness. When acid from the stomach comes up into a child's esophagus, it can cause inflammation and pain. It is important to note that not all patients with GERD visibly spit up. As long as the acid travels up the esophagus, it can cause the pain and fussiness of GERD. Symptoms include general fussiness, spitting up, increased fussiness when lying flat, and arching the back.

Enjoy the stage your child is in. It is okay to look forward to the future, but don't wish the present away.

Gordonian Wisdom

Why do so many babies spit up?
When adults or older children eat, a muscle at the top of the stomach called the lower esophageal sphincter tightens and prohibits the stomach contents from going into the esophagus. Babies universally have poorly developed lower esophageal sphincters and therefore all have some degree of gastroesophageal reflux. Fortunately, as children age, this usually resolves naturally.

To evaluate for GERD, many physicians will order an Upper GI. This is a radiology study done after the child drinks barium. Then serial x-rays are taken. The test lasts only 5 to 10 minutes. Some physicians wrongly consider this the diagnostic test for GERD. It is possible that a child with severe GERD may not show any episodes during the short study time. In my opinion, Upper GIs are overused and not needed to diagnose most cases of GERD. The diagnosis is made on history, physical exam and response to treatment.

Treatment of GERD in Infants:

Universal GERD recommendations:
1) Holding the infant upright for 30 minutes after feeding
2) Frequent burping during feeds
3) Elevating the head of his bed, so that he sleeps at a 30° angle.

Severe Cases of GERD May Require:

1) Adding rice or oatmeal cereal to the child's milk. This obviously requires more effort if the child is breastfeeding. The idea is increased viscosity can keep the milk in the stomach.

   Recently, I have backed off recommending thickening with rice cereal and prefer using oatmeal. I discuss my reasoning on page 86. Unfortunately, most of my experience and the research in this area has been done on rice cereal. To help with GERD, research indicates parents need to add at least one tablespoon of rice per ounce of milk. This amount of rice is impractical, as it is difficult, if not impossible, to pass this through a nipple. When I do recommend adding rice cereal, I start at one teaspoon per ounce of milk. Even with a third less rice cereal, parents often have to widen the nipple.

2) Zantac or other acid preventing medication. When children with GERD are fussy, I often prescribe Zantac. Zantac and other similar medications decrease the amount of acid produced in the stomach. For patients with reflux, less acid should mean less pain and fussiness. These acid preventing medications do not reduce the amount a child spits up, but they should reduce a GERD patient's pain. Always consult your doctor before giving your child medications.

   In pediatrics, the vast majority of cases of GERD will get better with time. As children grow, their diet becomes less liquid, they learn to walk upright and their stomach musculature (lower esophageal sphincter) matures. These factors lead to GERD symptoms naturally resolving between 6 to 18 months of age.

Two Weeks Circumcision Care

When do we start to retract our son's foreskin?

Immediately following the healing phase (two weeks), most children go through the "honeymoon phase" of circumcision healing. During the next few weeks, no special care is required for an individual's circumcision.

This phase ends when weight gain causes the remaining foreskin to rest on the penile head. At this time daily foreskin retraction should begin.

 Retract your son's remaining foreskin to avoid penile adhesions.

As children grow and gain weight, foreskin retraction becomes necessary. The length of time where regular retraction is required varies based on body type. Heavy individuals, especially those with fat around the penile area, will require retraction younger and often for more months. Typically, most circumcised boys need regular retraction from 2 to 18 months old. If done regularly, it causes no pain or discomfort. If retraction does not occur frequently, then bonds will form between the penile head and the remaining foreskin. Medically, we call these bonds "penile adhesions."

How to retract your son's foreskin

The cross-hatched area shows where the remaining foreskin is pushed forward to cover the edge of the penile head.

Using your thumb and pointer finger, gently retract your son's foreskin off the head of the penis.

Retraction is complete once you can see the red edge of the head of the penis.

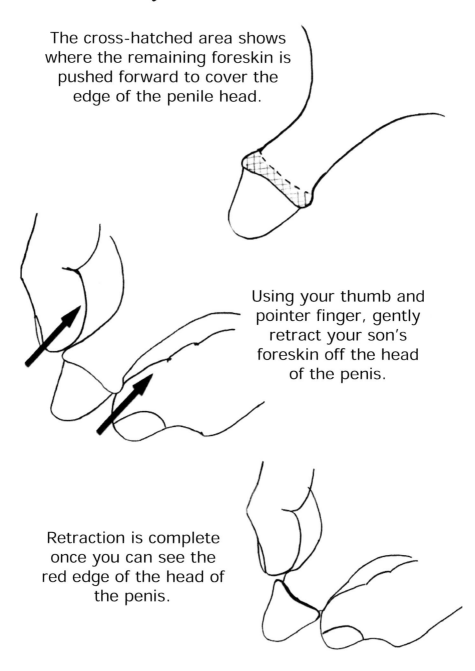

What are penile adhesions?

Many circumcised boys have penile adhesions. These are non-painful skin bridges that connect onto the penile head. Rarely, they develop immediately after circumcision secondary to procedure-related swelling. These post-surgical penile adhesions are difficult, if not impossible, to avoid. These adhesions should be addressed once the swelling has resolved (usually at the two week check up).

Most penile adhesions develop because of a lack of foreskin retraction in the first year of life. These adhesions are more common in heavy boys between the ages of 2 to 18 months. At these ages, many boys have extra fatty tissue which pushes the foreskin edge to partially or completely cover the penile head. If left undisturbed, the foreskin edge will attach to the head of the penis. Daily retraction of the foreskin will prevent these adhesions. As boys age and thin out, the propensity to acquire these adhesions naturally resolves.

There is some evidence that most penile adhesions will resolve given time, but that research is limited and not supported by large, prospective, double blind studies. Most experts agree that the mild ones will resolve and the strong "band" adhesions will require surgical intervention. It is difficult to advise parents of boys with "moderate" adhesions. Pediatricians and parents often must choose between minor discomfort involved in the release of the adhesion now verses observation and risking the chance that the adhesion will worsen with time.

Forced manual retraction of penile adhesions is controversial. Weak minor adhesions are not the issue. Often, minor adhesions are broken simply with gentle retraction. Retracting, or attempting retractions, is the only way to determine the presence and strength of the adhesion.

It is the act of breaking the stronger adhesions that is controversial. Breaking strong adhesions with manual force results in bleeding, discomfort and inflammation. During forced retraction of these adhesions, the physician will use both hands to break the adhesive bonds. Proponents of forced retraction believe that if left alone, adhesions will grow stronger with time. When adhesions are released, smegma becomes apparent. Smegma is a white colored debris that builds up between the penile head and foreskin.

Band Adhesions

In band adhe-
sions, a "band" of
foreskin tissue
adheres to the
head of the penis.

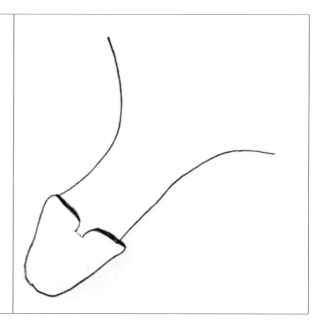

Complete Adhesions

Complete adhe-
sions "completely"
cover the edge of
the head of the
penis and cannot
be retracted.

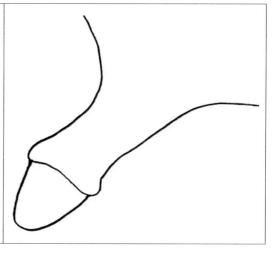

Many penile adhesions will resolve on their own, but some will not. Medical research thus far has been unable to delineate the difference. I tend to agree with the experts that believe most diffuse adhesions will self resolve, while the thicker band adhesions require medical or surgical treatment. All experts agree that proper circumcision care and education from the beginning is essential to avoid complications, decrease the risk of further procedures and ultimately yield the best outcome.

Concerns over the result of a boy's circumcision are extremely common. For a good circumcision result, you need both a good surgeon and good follow up care. I rarely see problems due to the actual procedure. Most of the circumcision complications occur secondary to poor long term care. Families are often unaware of the need for post-circumcision care. Penile adhesions are a common result of this lack of knowledge.

Despite being controversial, circumcision remains common in many areas of the world. Currently, many experts anticipate the WHO (World Health Organization) making its first medical recommendation in favor of circumcision. If this occurs, circumcision will be even more common.

Two Week Plagiocephaly

In the 1990s, the United States began the "Back to Sleep" program to reduce the risk of SIDS (Sudden Infant Death Syndrome). This program has been very effective at saving lives and has reduced the incidence of SIDS. Unfortunately, we have learned that placing children on their backs can lead to positional deformities of the skull. It is estimated that 22% of children in the United States will develop some degree of abnormal skull molding.

As a pediatrician, I have learned to look for abnormal head shape medically referred to as plagiocephaly. I frequently find children who have developed a symmetrical flat area in the back of their head. This variation of plagiocephaly seems to be the most common. These flat areas result from simply laying a child on firm, flat surfaces too often.
Often, cases of plagiocephaly are caused by a pulled or injured neck muscle. This muscular injury could occur in the womb, at delivery, or anytime the child's head is not well supported.

Closely monitor your child's head shape and ability to rotate his head

When an adult pulls a neck muscle, they consciously attempt to stretch it out. When babies pull a neck muscle, they choose to look the way that it does not hurt. As they keep their head turned, they begin to develop an off-center flat spot on the back of their head. If not corrected, this will worsen and begin to affect other areas of their skull. Given time, the muscular injury will get better, but the abnormal head shape could last.

The best way to evaluate a child for plagiocephaly is a "satellite view" as shown in this picture. This child has developed a flat occiput (back of the head).

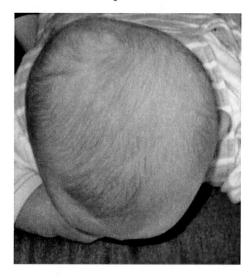

Therapy is centered around stretching out the pulled neck muscle to allow the head to rest in a more normal position. Breastfed infants are often forced to turn their heads both ways by feeding on both breasts. Formula fed infants whose parent feed the same way are often not forced to turn their heads both ways.

Addressing the Issue at Home:

1) Reverse how you feed your child. This is especially important for bottle fed children whose parents feed them the same way. Simply by switching hands, you can begin to correct the problem.

2) In most cases, I recommend gentle stretches with every diaper change. The two preferred stretches are turning the head from side to side in a

"no" pattern and from ear to shoulder. These stretches should not be forced. Stretches should be done when the child is relaxed and happy.

3) Minimize your child's time in car seats, swings and other "containers." When he is in his car seat, place your child's car seat toys toward the side that you want him to look.

4) When you place your baby in his crib, orient him so that he is encouraged to stretch his neck. This orientation forces him to self stretch if he wants to see desired objects. Place him in the crib such that when he wants to turn and look at the middle of the room he will be stretching the damaged muscle.

One of my boys had mild plagiocephaly secondary to a strained neck muscle. We saw the most improvement gently bouncing him around the house with his neck being stretched. When I held him, I would gently turn his head and bounce him for comfort.

If home stretching fails, some children will need physical therapy.

After the neck musculature improves, you usually see improvement in the child's head shape. In some cases, the plagiocephaly does not improve on its own. A referral to a pediatric neurosurgeon should be made between by six months of age if significant plagiocephaly continues. After an evaluation to rule out other abnormalities, the neurosurgeon may recommend the child wear a corrective helmet. These helmets must be custom designed to "round out" a child's head shape. Corrective helmets typically cost $2,000 to $3,000 and are generally not covered by insurance. Often, parents must weigh the cost of a helmet verses the likelihood of cosmetic deformity.

Two Months

Shortly after moving to Birmingham, Maggie and I discovered the Birmingham Zoo. The Zoo was close to our home, affordable and kid friendly. The day Eden was born so was a baby giraffe. After Eden was 2 months old, we bought annual passes. Maggie and Eden went weekly and watched the giraffe grow. Maggie has never been one to stay inside and firmly believes that children need to get outdoors. That winter it got unusually cold in Birmingham. One Saturday morning, Maggie insisted that we get out and go to the zoo. We bundled up and headed out. The streets were empty and so was the zoo parking lot. Fortunately, the zoo was open. There were few zoo visitor that day, but there was a local news crew. They were asking people why they were outdoors on a freezing cold day. When asked I basically said, "My wife made me go." While we were outside freezing, everyone else must have been home watching the news as the number of people that saw our interview seemed infinite.

Two Months Vaccines

Vaccines are the most controversial part of pediatric medicine. A generation ago, parents unquestionably accepted vaccines with little discussion of risks or benefits. Parents had personally been quarantined during polio outbreaks and

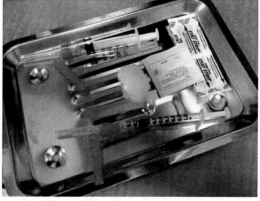

knew children who died from meningitis. Vaccination rates were the greatest among the highest educated patients.

Today, concerns and questions about vaccinations are normal. Vaccines' bad reputations can be directly linked to their effectiveness. Modern parents simply have not been exposed to these diseases. To them, measles occur only in third world countries and diphtheria exists only in the movie *Balto*.

Suddenly, unproven internet rumors seem more potentially harmful than the diseases that the vaccines protect against.

Anyone can make an accusation, but it is very difficult for the medical community to defend itself. Suppose a parent stated, "The vaccines Dr. X gave my son caused his hair to fall out." Dr. X is not legally allowed to discuss this child's case and defend himself, but the parents can make all the accusations they want. If public concern grows great enough, then research will be done. Unfortunately, it takes years and thousands of dollars to do the research needed to disprove rumors like this. By the time the research finally disproves the accusation, great damage will already be done as millions of people will have heard the untruth. In the end, research cannot entirely disprove an individual accusation, it can only effectively look at large populations.

In my first 15 years of pediatric practice, I've been asked about vaccines causing diseases, about individual vaccines causing autism, vaccine preservatives causing mercury poisoning and, most recently, about multiple vaccine doses causing a wide variety of problems. Fortunately, scientific research has disproven all of these theories. Unfortunately, many well-meaning parents have avoided or refused vaccination secondary to these disproven rumors. Most recently, parents are concerned about the number of vaccines given at each visit. Many parents are asking to split up the vaccines. Some self proclaimed "experts" are recommending their own baseless spaced out shot schedules. The problem with unique shot schedules is that they are not studied. When the AAP expert panel recommends a vaccine schedule, it is done based on the available safety and efficacy data. If you choose to ignore the recommended schedule, you may be exposing your child to increased risk or decreased vaccine efficacy.

In practice, I do allow families to split shots or even delay a vaccine for a few months. I fear that if I did not allow some flexibility, parents may choose to not vaccinate at all. Conversely, many pediatricians fear that tolerating vaccination delays, or allowing families to split vaccines validate these false rumors. While I agree that delayed vaccinations could lead to unnecessary infections and the spreading of diseases, these risks are minimal. I also agree that it is more challenging to deal with varied shot schedules to ensure maximal safety and efficacy for each patient.

Vaccines are a target for accusations primarily because nobody likes to get shots. Certainly, parents don't like to watch their children get shots. We, as a society, tend to blame things we dislike and excuse things that we do like. There are many other increasing societal trends. Why don't we blame unsolved health issues on increased consumption of artificial flavoring, remote controls, automobile use or cell phones?

Part of the public anxiety about vaccines stems from the very discussion of risk and benefits. I compare this to the "in the event of a water landing" information you hear after boarding a plane. If you weren't already nervous boarding a plane, let's talk about emergency exits, your oxygen mask and how your seat cushion can be used as a floatation device. In pediatrics, these full disclosure discussions of potential risks are important, but they heap on further stress to already nervous, tired parents.

Many parents get so focused on vaccine side effects, they fail to recognize the much greater risk of failing to vaccinate. As a parent, you are entitled to worry, question and doubt. But keep these concerns in prespective. I see many more complications from food allergens or insect bites than than vaccinations.

Bring acetaminophen to your child's check-ups.

Once your child is weighed we can give you an accurate dose prior to vaccination. See the dosing table on page 109.

There are two reasons to vaccinate your child:
1) to protect your child and
2) to protect our community.

Currently, the United States, overall vaccination rates are in the low 90 percentile range - with five or six percent of citizens unable or unwilling to be vaccinated. This rate of community protection prevents most diseases from circulating. Once the unvaccinated rate rises above ten percent, then diseases like pertussis and measles will begin to spread in our community. Immunosuppressed individuals (babies, pregnant women and the chronically ill) will no longer be protected. These individuals would be forced to either stay at home or risk potential fatal exposures in public.

I do not ask my patients to get vaccines my own children have not already had. My family and I have all been vaccinated as per the AAP schedule. I believe it is my parental duty to protect my family and, therefore, our community.

Two Months Growth Chart Basics

During each check up visit, your doctor should go over your child's growth and plot it on a growth chart. There are different growth charts for boys and girls. A child's length, weight and head circumference should be measured at check-ups in the first two years of life.

Let's take a quick tour of a growth chart. The one on the facing page addresses the length and weight for boys from birth to 24 months. There are two curves (groups of curved lines) on the previous page. As shown in the left margin, the top half addresses length and the bottom curve tracks weight. An individual is plotted on the chart based on his age (along the bottom edge) compared to his measurements (along the left edge).

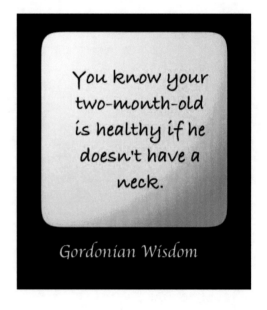

You know your two-month-old is healthy if he doesn't have a neck.

Gordonian Wisdom

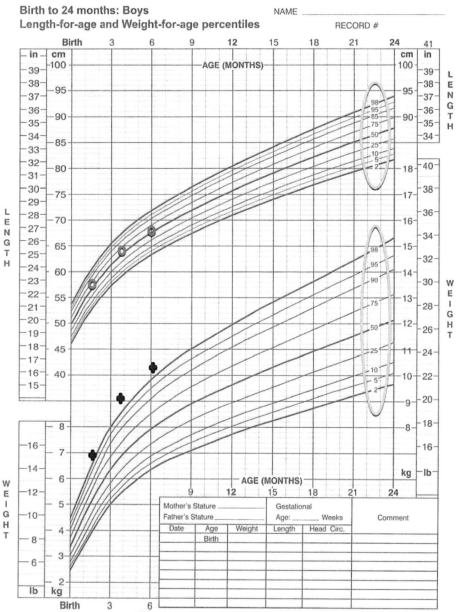

Birth to 24 months: Boys
Length-for-age and Weight-for-age percentiles

NAME _____

RECORD # _____

Published by the Centers for Disease Control and Prevention, November 1, 2009
SOURCE: WHO Child Growth Standards (http://www.who.int/childgrowth/en)

What does it mean that my son is fiftieth percentile for height?

Let's look at the upper height curve. Off to the right, circled in yellow, are numbers: 98, 95, 75, 50, 25, 10, 5, and 2. These are the percentiles associated with individual lines. These curved lines are called isobars.

The darkest line in the middle of the curve is the 50% line or average mark. Let's look at the upper height curve and the orange circles. The growth chart shown shows a 6-month-old whose height is growing along the 50th percentile. When a child at the 50th percentile on the growth chart is compared to 100 boys his age, half (or 50) would be taller and half (or 50) would be shorter.

What does "off the chart" mean?

Often, pediatricians will tell parents of large children that their child is "off the chart." "Off the chart" is only medical slang. It refers to the largest children growing above the 98th percentile. Likewise, "below the chart" refers to children growing below the 2nd percentile. Let's look at the blue plus signs on the lower part of the growth chart shown. Here, the 6-month-old depicted is "off the chart" or growing above the 98th percentile for weight.

When examining growth charts, it's more important where you end up than where you start. Many "small" 2-month-olds will grow into tall adults. Likewise, many huge "off the chart" 2-month-olds will become small adults. It is for this reason that I refer to the two month visit growth percentiles as starting positions.

> **Myth: You need to feed a baby solid foods to get him to sleep through the night.**
>
> **Truth: Medical research disproves this notion. All my children have learned to sleep through the night before three months and before they ever had solid foods.**

Ideally, children will establish their own curve and grow along an isobar. While I expect a given child to grow along the 25th percentile isobar, I would not expect him to be exactly 25th percentile each visit. Normal variation would allow a child to be 20th percentile on one visit and 35th at the next.

We expect children to grow to their genetic potential. Meaning most children will grow to be about the same size as their parents. Pediatricians worry when a child's growth is consistently declining or increasing beyond expectations.

Two Months Sleeping

Spacing it out (Step 2)

"Spacing it out" refers to slowly spacing apart a baby's feedings and nighttime sleeping stretches. By two months, many babies are "sleeping through the night." Spacing out feedings is important for all babies. For some families, it will be the final puzzle piece that leads to sleep. For all babies, spacing out feeding helps ease the daily routine and maintain good sleeping habits.

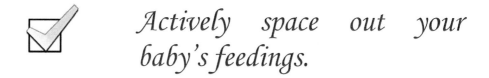

Actively space out your baby's feedings.

Spacing out Feedings for Sleep (Step 2)

At two months old, parents should begin to space out their baby's feedings. This can only begin once you have clearly established the right environment for sleep (stimulating daytime, boring nighttime and regular, predictable bedtime routine). As children age, the frequency of their feedings should decrease. While the feedings occur less often, the amount of milk should increase at each feeding. Newborns usually feed every two to three hours. By four months of age, term healthy babies should no longer require nighttime feedings and should only need to be fed every 3.5 to 4 hours.

Parent Question:

How do we space out our daughter's nursing frequency?

Begin by assessing her current schedule. Be honest. How often does she currently eat? Remember, nursing intervals are measured from the start of one feed to the start of the next feed. Suppose you discover she eats every 2.5 to 3 hours. Set a minimum, say two hours and 45 minutes. Encourage more milk at each feed. When she wants to feed at 2.5 hours you need to distract her for 15  minutes. This may mean walking outside, changing a diaper or offering a pacifier. Given time and consistency, she will adapt. As the two hours and 45 minute stretches become easy (usually one to two weeks later), increase your minimum to three hours.

Some babies will cluster feed before bedtime. Babies who cluster feed eat more frequently in the evenings followed by their longest sleeping stretch. If your baby cluster feeds and then sleeps well, stay with the cluster feeds. Simply space out her morning and afternoon feedings.

By gradually spacing out their feedings, children gradually increase their nighttime sleep stretches.

Parent Question:

What about nighttime feedings? Do these have to be spaced out as well?

Absolutely. When spacing out feedings, nighttime feedings are arguably the most important. You cannot teach a baby to sleep through the night by feeding him every two hours. Before feeding, make sure the minimum interval has passed and make sure your child is truly awake.

Waking after Two Months

There are two types of waking at this age:

1) Random wakings in a child with good established sleep habits
2) Chronic wakings in a child still developing good sleep habits.

If your child is consistently sleeping well and randomly wakes one night, go to him and assess him. Children that are sick or upset need to be comforted and cared for appropriately. Unfortunately, waking that develops from a valid reason (often illness or travel) will sometimes lead into bad sleep habits.

If your child is still learning to sleep through the night, or has developed a pattern of night wakings, remember the basics. Stay with your bedtime routine and keep daytime bright and nighttime dark and boring. When your baby wakes at this age, try not to feed him. It is easiest to simply feed your baby and go back to sleep, but this encourages future night wakings. When your child wakes up initially, try quick comfort measures to settle him back down. These interactions should be quick and without eye contact. Try giving a pacifier, repositioning or re-swaddling and walking out. Use a timer to keep yourself honest. If enough time has passed (on the timer) and your child does not settle back down, it is fine to feed.

After two months, there are really two time intervals that you should look at before deciding to feed your baby in the middle of the night:

1) Feeding Frequency Time - If you are spacing out a baby's feeding frequency to three hours - you should not feed that baby until at least three hours have passed.

2) Minimum Feeding Delay - We discourage our babies from feeding at night by delaying their feedings. We don't feed him immediately upon

awakening, but delay his feeding with other comfort measures. These are not long "cry it out" times, they are shorter. This usually starts at 15 minutes, but can grow from there. By delaying feedings, children may fall back to sleep.

During night wakings, we check on our babies in intervals. Suppose your 3-month-old wakes tonight. After two minutes of fussing, enter the room and try a few quick comfort methods. If your baby continues to cry, continue to try these quick comfort methods at increasing intervals. Begin with two minutes and work yourself up to four to five minute intervals. If both your feeding frequency time interval and minimum feeding delay has passed and your baby is still crying, feed him and return him to his bed.

Myth: Breastfed babies can't sleep through the night without some formula.

Truth: Breastfed babies sleep just as well as formula fed babies.

Minimizing Nighttime Feedings

If your child is still not sleeping despite a bright, stimulating day, a dark, boring night, a consistent bedtime routine and every 3.5 to 4 feedings is critical to sleeping through the night. After two months, some families must begin the difficult task of actively ending nighttime feedings. The initial goal is to establish a six hour feeding free stretch. Start by examining your child's sleep/feeding schedule. Work with your child's longest natural stretch and try to extend it. For our children, their longest stretch was after their bedtime routine. Just like stretching out daytime feedings, work in 15 minute goals. If your 3-month-old's longest stretch is currently four hours, initially try to increase the feeding free time to four hours and fifteen minutes. As when stretching out daytime feedings, you may need to offer a pacifier, re-swaddle or bounce to make it those extra few minutes. Once four hours and 15 minutes gets easy, try for 4.5 hours.

This middle of the night "work" is difficult; you may need to use a timer to keep yourself honest. Realize that a few nights of reduced sleep will pay off with a lifetime of good sleep habits.

Rolling over and SIDS

Parent Question:

Our son was down to only waking up once a night and now has reverted to waking up every two to three hours. Randomly, he was put down for a nap on his tummy and slept better than he had in two weeks. I know that "back is best" but since he is over six months, can lift his head and can roll over on his own, is there any issue with tummy sleeping?

I agree that most children sleep best on their tummies (prone position) and that most cases of SIDS (Sudden Infant Death Syndrome) occur prior to six months of age (over 90%). However, to reduce the risk of SIDS I recommend parents place their children on their backs to sleep. Once children are able to roll over (completely on their own) and sleep prone, then it is safe. It is impossible for parents to keep flipping their child over repetitively all night long (though many have tried). Additionally, there is an increased risk of SIDS in children who normally sleep on their back and then are placed prone. Place him on his back, but allow him to flip over if he chooses. If your child chooses to sleep prone, he should no longer be swaddled.

A pediatrician's medical views are often shaped by their own experiences. I know a couple of my experienced partners that would tell you to simply let him sleep on his tummy. Unfortunately, I cannot. During my residency, I knew a pediatrician who had four children. One night he and his wife placed their baby on his stomach to calm him down and he died. I doubt they caused his death, but I do know that they will always blame themselves. It is simply not worth it.

Swaddling for Sleep

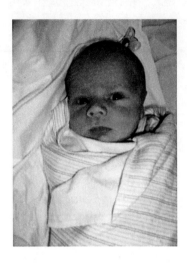

Parent Question:

My son is three months old. We are still swaddling him when he sleeps. Is this OK? He doesn't seem to have good control over his movements, and he will wake himself up if not swaddled.

Swaddling beyond two months old is a controversial subject. We usually swaddle our children until four to six months old. Overall, swaddling (when done correctly) is beneficial to children and a practice I would encourage.

There are some experts that worry swaddling after two months may increase a child's risk for SIDS (Sudden Infant Death Syndrome). These experts are concerned that after two months, a swaddled child could increase his risk of SIDS by rolling over or covering his head with the blanket. While these are valid concerns, there is currently insufficient evidence to support them.

 Swaddle your baby.

In fact, current evidence shows that swaddling and placing a baby supine (on his back) reduces the risk of SIDS. Swaddling an infant and placing him prone (on his stomach) clearly increases risk of SIDS. In 2006, Pediatrics published Swaddling: A Systematic Review. This review concluded "There is an increased risk of SIDS, but only when the swaddled infant is placed prone or is able to turn to the prone position." It is critical to differentiate between swaddling and placing supine verses swaddling and placing prone. While this seems obvious, this important difference is not apparent to many swaddling critics. In 2009, Dr. Bradley Thach wrote a review article for the Journal of Pediatrics entitled "Does Swaddling Decrease or Increase the Risk of Sudden Infant Death Syndrome?" In this review, he found only one article showing an apparent increase in SIDS in swaddled children. Furthermore, he found that that this study "did not distinguish between swaddled when prone vs. infant's swaddled supine."

Another swaddling issue concerns the proper duration of swaddling. The only research on swaddling duration seems to focus at cultural variations. The AAP, as of yet, does not have an official recommendation on the proper swaddling duration. Currently, experts vary in the recommendations on how long parents should swaddle their children. I know a few experts are now recommending against swaddling or to stop swaddling at two months old. I question if that is what they did for their children. There is risk in swaddling. But there is also risk in not swaddling. Too often expert recommendations are driven less by fact and more by fear of lawsuits. Clearly, it is safe to swaddle children until they learn to roll over. We swaddled our children for four to six months. Although as they got closer to four months old, we usually did not swaddle their arms. Around this age, most of our children preferred to have their arms free. Our youngest daughter was swaddled until she was five months old. She clearly enjoyed being swaddled and preferred to stay on her back for sleep.

Fever Three Months

For children over the age of three months, a fever is a temperature of 101°F or higher. Oral or rectal temperature readings are the best and the gold standard and used in research. For practical reasons, we often will take axillary (under arm) temperatures. Many people will add to axillary temperatures to compensate for its inaccuracies. I prefer my patients to report the number and how they took the temperature.

The general rule of thermometers: the fancier the thermometer, the less accurate. We do not own ear, forehead or temporal thermometers.

Fever itself should not be a scary thing. Our own bodies create elevated temperatures to fight off infections. It is more important how your child is acting than the actual number reading on the thermometer. Children are often only mildly sick with a 104°F temperature. On the other hand, children can be seriously ill with a 100.4°F temperature.

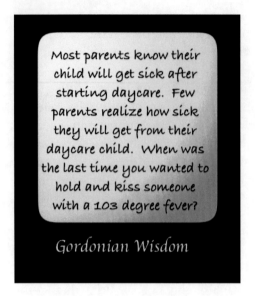

Most parents know their child will get sick after starting daycare. Few parents realize how sick they will get from their daycare child. When was the last time you wanted to hold and kiss someone with a 103 degree fever?

Gordonian Wisdom

Parents are often afraid of fevers and nervous about illness. I'd *like* to say we were better when our first child had her first illness. I was in my pediatric internship on nights in the emergency department. In my training program, our emergency department rotation always included a week of seven consecutive twelve hour nights - from 7 p.m. to 7 a.m. I had arrived home after work and fell asleep. After 45 minutes of sleep, Maggie woke me up in a panic. Our daughter had a fever, and we needed to get to our pediatrician as soon as possible. We drove directly to the office. I remember beginning to wake up at our pediatrician's office. It was completely ridiculous. Our daughter was acting well overall and had been sick for about 20 minutes. I'm sure our pediatrician chuckled that we even brought her in - and laughed that it was "an emergency visit."

Four Months

The day our first-born turned four months, we started solid foods. My wife read one parenting book on the topic and consulted several family members. We started with a week of rice cereal mixed with breast milk, then proceeded to Stage 1 fruits. One afternoon, Maggie began to read another parenting book. This book advised feeding vegetables first so that children did not prefer sweet foods. Maggie went into "new parent panic mode," certain she had ruined our precious daughter. She called me at work and asked

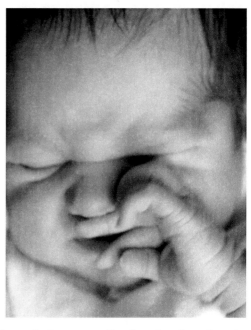

my professional opinion. I graduated from medical school only six months earlier and knew a lot about chest tube insertion in premature babies, but nothing about feeding solids. Yet another chance to impress my wife with my great pediatric knowledge blown. Her panic lead her to read multiple books on starting solids. Each book disagreed with the prior book. Finally, it became clear to us that there is not one "right" way to feed solids.

Gregory Gordon, MD

Four Months Feeding

When should you start solids?

First children never learn to roll over "on time" because everyone holds them too much.

Gordonian Wisdom

I often joke that if you asked ten pediatricians, read ten books and asked ten grandmothers, you would get thirty different opinions on when to start solid foods. During my residency, the American Academy of Pediatrics (AAP) recommended initiating solid feedings at four months old. Since then, researchers have examined the allergic and immunologic consequences of these choices. Many groups have advocated waiting on solid food until six months or even later.

Currently, the AAP gives a mixed opinion on when to start solids. The "Section on Breastfeeding" currently recommends exclusive breastfeeding for six months while the "Committee on Nutrition and Section on Allergy and Immunology" recommends starting solids at four to six months.

One of the big movements in medicine is for "evidence based medicine." That is, making medical decisions rooted by the purest evidence. A leader in this effort is the Cochrane Collaboration. The Cochrane Collaboration examines all current medical research and then creates evidence based reviews. These reviews are unbiased and considered the best in medical circles. In 2011, the Cochrane Collaboration examined the optimal duration of exclusive breastfeeding. They did find some minimal benefits to exclusively breastfeeding for six months compared to three months. They concluded:

> "Exclusive breastfeeding for six months (versus three to four months, with continued mixed breastfeeding thereafter) reduces gastrointestinal infection and helps the mother lose weight and prevent pregnancy but has no long-term

impact on allergic disease, growth, obesity, cognitive ability, or behavior."

Excerpt from **The Cochane Collaboration**

Over the past 10 years, breastfeeding advocates and the AAP have convinced most parents and our youngest generation of pediatricians that starting solid foods at four months is harmful to children. Current evidence does not support these concerns.

After carefully reviewing a mixed bag of research, I recommend beginning solids between four to six months old. (I'll explain more of my thinking on this issue in several related sections.)

 Solid foods should be started when children are four to six months old.

What solids should you feed a baby first?

Early in my pediatric career, this was an easy question. Most experts have universally recommended starting with rice cereal. Rice cereal is fortified with iron and hypoallergenic. I've heard it said that "no one is allergic to rice." In 2012, Consumer Reports published a study on arsenic contamination of rice. Since then, myself and other physicians have backed off recommending rice.

If you surveyed grandmothers as to what to feed first:

- 35% would recommend vegetables (Often the stated reason is that if you feed sweet fruits first, they won't learn to like veggies)

- 30% would suggest fruits (Often the stated reason is that if you feed sweet fruit first, they will like to eat and always be a "good eater")

- 30% would recommend a variety of grains (rice, oatmeal, wheat, barley, etc.)

- 5% would say in their day, they started their babies on ribs, chicken wings and steak.

Our first seven children were started on rice cereal mixed with breast milk and then proceeded to fruits and vegetables. After discussing the rice issue, Maggie and I decided to skip rice and begin our youngest child on fruits or veggies. Four days after our eighth child turned four months old, one of our older sons turned thirteen years old. His birthday wish was to be the first person to feed his little sister solids. His wish was granted. He was the first to feed his sister. We also let him choose which fruit or veggie to feed. He choose squash. Maggie and I agree that squash is probably a good first food and also that the choosing of the right first food is not critical.

If you choose to start with rice, begin with three or four tablespoons of rice cereal. Then mix it to a runny oatmeal consistency, warm it slightly in the microwave, remix and test for temperature. If you follow the directions on the box it will end up too runny.

We feed our young children in a bouncy seat until they are able to sit well on their own. We feed them with a small plastic coated spoon once or twice a day. Typically, the first few feedings end up all over the place. This should be fun. If it's a miserable experience, stop and retry in a few weeks.

Should a child starting solids drink less milk?

Parents who make their own baby foods should purchase a couple of store brand baby foods to demonstrate the desired consistency.

No. Typically, a child's milk intake stays the same when they start solids. When starting solids, children are poor eaters and consume few calories through solid feedings. Formula fed infants average 25 to 35 ounces a day from four to nine months old. Solid feedings are part nutrition and part oral motor practice. Early on, a large portion of spoon fed solids come out of the child's mouth. Given time, children learn to use their lips and tongue in a more coordinated manner. This oral motor "work out" develops muscle strength and coordination for more complicated foods and speech development. In the beginning, solids should be fed when children are not hungry. A hungry 5-month-old simply eats too slowly to be satisfied by a solid feeding. Feed your child milk first and then offer the solid foods.

Feeding on Demand vs. Schedule

Parent Question*:*

I was wondering what you (and/or your wife) believe as far as breastfeeding on demand versus more on a schedule. Our 4-month-old was doing really well sleeping through the night without nursing, but has now reverted (after being sick). I've been letting her nurse on demand lately in an attempt to increase my milk supply, which I feel is low.

In general, we keep a loose schedule. We work toward a schedule, but work with the baby to get there. I do not believe in complete on demand feedings (at this age) or strict parent directed feedings. During, and shortly following illness, we often ended up more toward the "on demand" side. I would not feed a 4-month-old more than every three hours. Another way to increase milk supply is to pump immediately after the baby nurses. Even if you are only able to pump a little extra milk, your body should begin to produce more. Stick with a rigid bedtime routine and try not to feed her when she wakes at night. If, after bedtime, you have to feed or hold her, do as little as you can. As children recover from illness, they typically feed better, which should, in turn, help your milk supply. With time and persistence, you should be sleeping and back to a more normal schedule soon.

Should 4-month-olds be given extra iron?

Formula fed infants do not need extra iron. This concern is relative only to breastfed infants.

The best eyelashes are wasted on boys.

Gordonian Wisdom

Interest in iron deficiency has increased recently, secondary to reports of cognitive delays associated with low iron levels. The AAP committee on nutrition examined the current evidence surrounding iron deficiency. In October of 2010, the American Academy of Pediatrics issued a report called "Diagnosis and Prevention of Iron Deficiency and Iron-Deficiency Anemia in Infants and Young Children (0–3 Years of Age)." They found that exclusively breastfed infants reached low iron levels between four to six months of age. They concluded that breastfed infants should be supplemented or fed vitamins until iron containing solid foods are introduced.

> "Therefore, at four months of age, breastfed infants should be supplemented with one mg/kg per day of oral iron beginning at four months of age until appropriate iron-containing complementary foods (including iron-fortified cereals) are introduced in the diet."
>
> ***American Academy of Pediatrics*** *website* _www.aap.org_

The AAP committee on breastfeeding recently reaffirmed its recommendation for parents to withhold solid feedings in breastfed infants until six months of life. Therefore, a family strictly following current AAP guidelines would place their breastfed 4-month-old on vitamins for two months prior to starting solid foods.

I do agree with the AAP committee findings and concerns about the neurologic consequences of iron deficiency anemia. I disagree, however, with their recommendations for artificial vitamins at this age. I am a strong believer that breastfeeding is natural and best. I do believe the drop in breastfed 4-month-old's serum iron levels is real. This finding does not explain a known problem clinically seen in breastfed children. Severe iron deficiency can cause "cognitive slowing" or loss of IQ points. The contrary appears to be true in breastfed children. Breastfed children are one to two IQ points higher than their formula fed counterparts.

I choose to view the decrease in 4-month-old's iron levels as real medical evidence that all parents should start solid foods at this age. I would rather give my 4-month-old pureed green beans than vitamins made in a factory. The idea that vitamins are superior to naturally iron-rich vegetables is much like the idea that man-made is superior to all natural. Just like formula fed children, breastfed children should be fed solid foods between four to six months. Breastfeeding parents should specifically encourage iron containing foods.

How many times a day should you feed solids to your baby?

Between four to six months old, children only need to be fed once or twice a day. At this stage, children can be fed separately from family meal time. Between six to nine months, children will begin to intently watch and even scream for food while their parents are eating. As this natural desire increases, parents are often "forced" to include children in meals. By nine months old, children should be fed three times a day and be included in family meal time.

When during the day should you feed solids to your baby?

This sounds backwards, but when starting solids, babies should be fed solids when they are not hungry. Solids should be fed shortly after a bottle or nursing. When starting solids, these feedings are more entertainment and oral motor practice than a major source of nutrients. Hungry, crying babies calm down as soon as they get some milk. Milk offers a quick calorie source. Early on, babies are inefficient solid eaters. If you take a 4-month-old who slept all night and offer him rice cereal, you will quickly have a crying frustrated baby. Early on, solids must come after milk. First, feed your child a full feeding of breast milk or formula, after he is satisfied, offer him solids.

How much should you feed your child?

The amount of solids fed to a child should vary by individual and slowly increase with age. Some children "love" solids and other don't. When starting out, our 4 to 5-month-olds take the equivalent of one jar of Stage 1 baby foods (2.5 ounces) in each feeding.

As children grow, their need for solids increases. Children are typically ready for Stage 2 consistency foods around six months. Stage 2 foods are 4 ounces and a good "meal size" for children six to nine months. Our youngest daughter enjoyed solid foods more than any of her siblings. At seven months, she would eat two to three Stage 2 containers at dinner. During the first half of her solids, she ate as quickly as we could feed her.

Does early introduction of solid foods cause allergies?

When our first child was born, we struggled to find the "right" way to introduce solid foods. Our family members recommended starting solids at four months, but they disagreed on what to feed. Some books recommended starting with vegetables and others starting with fruits. We wanted to do things right and were perplexed by "experts" that contradicted each other.

Unfortunately, feeding advice has only become more muddied since then. Not only do "experts" argue *what* to feed first, but *when* to start solids. The last 10 years have been filled with research investigating the relationships of these early feedings with allergic problems.

Thankfully, we are starting to get some clarity on these issues. It is best to start solid feeding between four to six months old.

There is no clear evidence that feeding children solid foods at four months of age causes food allergies, eczema, seasonal allergies or asthma.

Yes, there is some research that suggests that there may be a link between the timing of certain foods and allergic problems (atopic disease). However, the majority of research finds no link, and some research shows that waiting to introduce solid foods may increase the risk of allergic disease.

The American Academy of Pediatrics Committee on Nutrition and Section on Allergy and Immunology recently concluded the same, stating:

> "Although solid foods should not be introduced before four to six months of age, there is no current convincing evidence that delaying their introduction beyond this period has a significant protective effect on the development of atopic disease."
>
> ***Pediatrics** Vol. 121 No. 1 January 1, 2008, pp. 183 -191.*

They go on to state that the lack of evidence even applies to delaying known food allergens.

> "This includes delaying the introduction of foods that are considered to be highly allergic, such as fish, eggs and foods containing peanut protein."

These solid food feeding recommendations apply equally to formula and breastfed children. Basically, after a period of intense research, we have once again learned to listen to grandma. "Relax and feed your baby at four to six months of age."

Do you start one food at a time?

When starting out, it is a good idea to introduce one new food every five to seven days. Most experts will tell you that starting this way will help detect food allergies. Practically speaking, this rarely occurs. Few babies are allergic to grains, fruits and veggies. Common non-allergic food problems like constipation, diaper and facial rashes will be discussed in future chapters.

I support the idea of introducing food varieties slowly as even babies prefer familiar foods. Our babies often dislike new food, but learn to like them over a few days. It is this reaction that has led us to feed a new food with a familiar favorite. When starting new solid foods, the new food should be fed each day during the five day period. Any foods previously tolerated can be included in a meal.

While most people recommend either veggies or fruits, we alternate (roughly), adding fruits then vegetables. We quickly end up with fruits in the morning and veggies in the evening.

Let me explain…

Our first 5-day period, we'll choose squash. We feed squash once or twice a day (and take lots of pictures)

During the second 5-day period, we add a fruit (say, apple sauce). During these five days, apple sauce is fed once or twice a day. We may feed apple sauce for breakfast and squash for dinner. Sometimes we will include squash along with the apple sauce. The two foods are kept on separate sides of a bowl. Our new eaters often pucker their lips and make faces when fed a new unfamiliar taste. When upset about the apple sauce, we will offer a few spoonfuls of the squash (the familiar food). Introducing new food is easier by introducing a new taste with a familiar "comfort" food.

During the third 5-day period, we would introduce either another veggie or grain (say rice cereal). During this third period, rice cereal would be fed every day. We might feed meals of apple sauce with rice in the morning, and squash with rice is fed at night. We could have a big meal, including squash, rice cereal and apple sauce if we wanted.

During the fourth 5-day period, we will start green beans (never a favorite of our babies). Of course, every day we will feed green beans. During these five days, breakfast would remain apple sauce with or without rice cereal. Green beans would be fed at dinner with or without squash or rice cereal.

This is not a rigid list of the exact foods we feed, because it varies with each child. The principles stay the same. New fruits get cycled in at breakfast, while new veggies get cycled in at dinner. We feed grains any time of day.

Parents often ask for the precise written instructions of what to feed their babies. When we were new parents, I know we wanted the "right foods list," too. Unfortunately, there is not a single correct way to feed children.

Talk to your family and friends, ask your pediatrician and read a few books. Then make your best decision for your child.

Rice and Arsenic

Parent Question:

Our fourth baby is curious about table foods and I'm ready to start her on solids. I've come across a number of articles about arsenic in rice cereal and am considering skipping rice altogether. Do you agree with this, and if so, do I forego cereals altogether and go straight to vegetables and fruits -- or should we try oat cereal, etc.?

In the past ten years, rice cereal was encouraged by experts concerned about food allergies. Rice cereal was touted as "hypoallergenic." Our first seven children were fed rice cereal as a first food. Now there is a growing body of evidence that rice cereal and many other rice products contain arsenic.

In 2012, Consumer Reports found that rice and numerous rice-containing products contained arsenic. Many of these products are trusted household brands like Kellogg's, Uncle Ben's, Quaker and Gerber. Additional research has found higher arsenic levels in individuals who consume rice products.

Arsenic is a naturally occurring element known to be poisonous and carcinogenic. Until the 1980s, arsenic was used as a pesticide in commercial agriculture. Plants grown in soil contaminated with arsenic will pick it up. This is not limited to rice. In fact, arsenic can be found in some vegetables, fruits and fruit juices.

As anxiety grew among American consumers the industry responded. The USA Rice Federation stated that there is no reason for concern about United States grown rice, arguing that "there is no documented evidence of actual adverse health effects from exposure to arsenic in U.S.-grown rice." Many companies have responded to consumers concerns. Gerber currently states on their website:

"Therefore, earlier this year, we decided to exclusively use California rice in all of our rice-containing dry infant cereal. We chose California rice because California has the lowest arsenic levels for rice grown in the United States."

www.gerber.com

To make matters more confusing, there are currently no established federal limits to define the safe level of arsenic in foods. Under increased community interest in the fall of 2012, the FDA announced that they are actively investigating arsenic levels in foods. Currently, they do not recommend that consumers change their eating habits while awaiting further scientific research.

Practically speaking, there have been no epidemics of arsenic poisoning or dramatic increases in the rates of cancer thought related to arsenic. Agricultural arsenic use ended almost 30 years ago. Logically speaking, peak arsenic levels would have occurred in the 1980s. Meaning our generation was exposed to the highest levels of arsenic in our food. By this reasoning, the arsenic doses should decrease with every crop.

I am hopeful that the FDA will eventually determine scientific based recommendations regarding arsenic levels in our diet. Until then, we must make rational decisions based on known information. In general, rice products should be avoided in young children, but children and adults can continue to eat a modest amount.

My recommendations based on the available research:

1) Eat a wide variety of non-processed foods. I will continue to eat and serve my children a modest amount of rice and rice containing products.

2) Rice cereal should no longer be an infant's first food. Children should start with fruits, vegetables or other grains, such as barley and oatmeal.

3) Rice should no longer be a high percentage of a young child's diet. It is OK to feed your child some rice cereal. It should not be fed daily. Parents should no longer use rice cereal to thicken formulas or breast milk. This is often done to help alleviate symptoms of GERD. Oatmeal can serve as a reasonable alternative. Parents should avoid formulas sweetened with brown rice syrup. Brown rice syrup is often

used in organic baby products. Families looking for an alternative to cow's milk should choose something other than rice milk for their children.

Can I give my baby water?

There is little need to give children water in the first several months of life. Young children need either breast milk or formula. Excess water can decrease a baby's serum sodium concentration and lead to seizures. The classic case is of a financially struggling family who opts to dilute their baby's formula to save money. I admitted a baby with this classic scenario during my residency. Today, thanks to public education and government provided formula, the situation is extremely rare.

Children can have a small amount of water starting at four months.

In the heat of the summer, many of my patient's parents ask about giving water on hot days. After four months, I am okay with giving some extra water to healthy well grown children beyond four months old. My rule of thumb is children can have the same number of ounces of water per day as they are old in months. Such that a 5-month-old can have five ounces of water a day.

When can you give a baby juice?

It is safe to give juice to children four months and older. The bigger question is, *"Should you give your child juice?"*

Juice is predominantly sugar. Children seem to quickly enjoy and even crave juice. In pediatrics, excess juice intake is a common nutritional cause of poor growth. Juice seems to be enough to quench a child's hunger, but it not enough to help him grow. Children simply do not need juice.

One of our older children became "juice addicted" as a toddler. She would drink two glasses of juice in the morning and completely skip breakfast. She learned to stand at the fridge and beg. The begging ended only after we quit buying apple juice. Months later, we re-introduced juice without any problems.

When children are constipated, I often recommend prune, apple or white grape juice. I prefer to start with dietary modification, like this, before initiating constipation medications. When using juice to help alleviate constipation, do not mix it with water. The sugars in juice draw in extra water into the intestines and lead to softer stools.

Juice can be served to children starting at four months.

At our home, we prefer to wait 9 to 12 months before introducing juice as a regular part of our children's diet. We restrict juice to 2 to 6 ounces a day at breakfast.

Constipation when Starting Solids

Parent Question:

We started my daughter on some solids after her 4-month-old appointment. We started with rice cereal mixed with breast milk. She loves it, but we think it makes her constipated. She went from pooping a couple of times per day to pooping every couple of days and it was thicker. Should we try oatmeal cereal instead, give her some baby food prunes every day along with the cereal, or maybe just quit with the solids altogether for a while? Is the cereal definitely necessary for iron?

The immediate issue is, *"What should we feed her right now?"* I would recommend you put a hold on the rice cereal and just breastfeed for another one to two weeks. If she is still having painful, hard ball or clay stools, I would add four ounces of undiluted apple juice. After her stools are more regular, I would proceed with non-banana fruits.

I like juice as a tool to help with constipation, but I would not recommend juice otherwise. We pediatricians often see children that "get addicted to juice" and drink it all day long. Juice has little nutritional content, but can fill children up enough that they do not eat the milk/food they need.

After getting started with a few fruits, you could then introduce some green veggies like peas or green beans which contain iron. In our office, we typically check a CBC (complete blood count via a finger prick) at nine months. The CBC is intended to pick up cases of iron deficiency anemia.

Oatmeal is not necessarily better for constipation than rice cereal. After she has tolerated several fruits and veggies, I would retry the rice cereal slowly. While I agree the rice cereal is likely the cause of her current constipation, I'll bet she will eventually tolerate it without issue.

If you think you smell poop - you do. And eventually you will find it.

Gordonian Wisdom

Four Months Sleep

Four-month-old Close to Sleeping Well

The first morning a baby sleeps through the night, all parents wake up startled and certain their baby has been kidnapped.

Gordonian Wisdom

Parent Question:

What should we do with our 4-month-old son who is close to sleeping through the night? We came upon your website only a month ago and have been working to improve his sleep habits. We have a well established bedtime routine, he is now 14 pounds, and he eats every 3 to 3.5 hours. He now only wakes up once to twice a night.

Remember, our goal is a consistent six to eight hour stretch. He may already be giving you that. If his longest stretches without eating are at night, then I agree he is doing great. This is a starting point, and I'm sure you are hoping for longer stretches. Continue to gradually space out his daytime feedings - working toward every four hours. Minimize your interactions in the middle of the night - don't feed him unless you have to. Offer a pacifier, pat his back, re-swaddle and try and make a consistent six hour stretch. Given consistent effort and increased weight, he should establish good sleep habits.

Sleeping in Swings and Car Seats

Parent Question:

Out of pure desperation for more sleep, I placed my 4-month-old in the swing to sleep at night. He went from sleeping two to three hour stretches to six to eight hours. It is four weeks later. With a few unsuccessful attempts to have him sleep in his own crib, I find myself just placing him straight into the swing at night to sleep. What are your thoughts on infants sleeping in swings for long periods of time? Am I doing any damage other than prolonging his ability to learn to sleep without motion??

I doubt you are causing your son any harm, but he clearly cannot sleep in his swing forever. His swing will soon be unsafe. There is no set age where swings are unsafe; this depends on the type of swing and the size of your son. Swing use usually needs to end around six months. At this age, my son who loved his swing learned to hold and stop the swing. He was large enough that his rapid movements made the swing unstable.

Ideally, you could slowly transition him out of the swing and into a crib. The difficult part is finding a slow transition that will work for your son. Will he sleep any other way? Even a small variation would be a step forward. What happens if you stop the swing? Can you transfer him to his crib after he falls asleep? Does he sleep in his car seat or stroller? I would continue to work toward an easy transition for the next two months.

While a slow gentle transition sounds ideal, I predict you are in for a struggle. If you are unable to find a smooth transition, you are going to have to let him cry to learn to fall asleep on his own. Eventually, all children need to learn to fall asleep on their own and settle themselves down when they wake up in the middle of the night. When working with children six months and older who cannot settle themselves down, I recommend "crying it out." See the Crying it Out section at six months on page 100.

You need to make sure you have done all of the sleep basics: bright and stimulating day, dark and boring night, strict bedtime routine and spacing out his feedings. You may even add some crib time to his bedtime routine. His routine might be: feed, bath, dress, feed a little more, give pacifier, place in crib with parent at bedside comforting for five minutes and then place in swing. Hopefully, he will learn to sleep in his crib with persistent, gentle measures. If he isn't sleeping better by six months then I would "cry it out."

Teaching Your Child to Fall Asleep on His Own (Step 3)

Placing in the crib awake

The process of teaching your child to sleep is complete once your awake child is placed in his crib and he sleeps all night. Often, children will have mastered this by four months. Unfortunately, many children who sleep through the night at four months will develop a pattern of night wakings. This pattern of sleeping all night followed by regular night wakings is typical for children who failed to learn to settle themselves down. To maintain good sleep habits, children need to be placed in their beds awake and put themselves to sleep. These wakings occur between six to nine months in children who are regularly rocked or nursed to sleep. These children believe they are unable to put themselves back to sleep - so they cry for their parents.

 Teach your child to fall asleep on his own.

To prevent these night wakings, try to place your baby in his bed while still groggy. Most children who have been on a steady bedtime routine will accept being placed in their bed and fall asleep easily. If your child cries, initially offer a pacifier or soothing words. If he continues to cry, you can hold him until he's asleep and then transfer him. It is important to try and continue to retry. Fortunately, this is easy for families who have established the right environment for sleep. When children fail to learn to fall asleep on their own by six months, "crying it out" is the best method for help.

Gregory Gordon, MD

Was Sleeping through the Night

Parent Question:

Our 8-month-old daughter quit sleeping through the night. We had followed your advice and it worked. We did and still do the dark, boring night, the bright, stimulating day and a strict bedtime routine. Initially, it worked and she was sleeping eight hours nightly before two months old. For the last three weeks, she now wakes up every four hours. I don't have to feed her, but I do have to pick her up, give her her pacifier and rock her to sleep. We took her to our pediatrician, and he said her ears are not infected. Please help.

This is an extremely common situation that develops between six to nine months old. She is waking because she has not learned to fall asleep on her own. My guess is that every night, you end your bedtime routine by rocking her and giving her a pacifier. She is now waking in the night and wants to go back to sleep. So she cries for you, as she thinks she needs you to fall asleep. Stop rocking her to sleep! End your bedtime by placing her tried, but still awake in her bed. Hopefully, this will work. This is usually easier to start when children are two months old, rather than six months. If she screams and cannot settle herself down, you may need to *cry it out.* (See the six months section on page 100).

Six Months

Shortly after our second child, Isaac, was born, our daughter Eden turned two. Maggie took Isaac everywhere she took his 2-year-old sister. He often took naps in the car and helped Maggie drop off his big sister at her "mother's morning out" program. Maggie also took him to the park to watch Eden burn off some energy. When Isaac was six months old, Maggie discovered he loved going to the park. He could not crawl and was strapped into a stroller, but he still loved the playground. Watching all the "big kids" running, jumping and swinging was stimulating. At this time, the park became a favorite family activity. Eden loved to play with her friends, Isaac loved to watch them, and Maggie loved the long naps that happened afterward. We laugh, as prior to having a second child, neither of us would have thought that a stroller bound 6-month-old would enjoy going to a playground.

Six Months Feeding

If fathers changed all the diapers in the world, there would be more wipes but less diapers in landfills.

Gordonian Wisdom

The six to nine month period involves dramatic dietary changes. At six months, some children are taking a variety of Stage 1 foods and some children have not started solid foods. By nine months, most children are able to eat a variety of table foods. Six to 9-month-old children still rely on formula or breast milk as their major calorie source; usually drinking 25 to 35 ounces a day.

Children who have not started solids should begin with some Stage 1 fruits and vegetables. Children who have already mastered Stage 1 foods can begin Stage 2 foods or homemade pureed foods. Stage 2 foods are courser than Stage 1. We also begin to offer some table foods that are "baby food" consistency - mashed potatoes, apple sauce or guacamole. During this stage, our children often like to hold the spoon and try to feed themselves. While this is fun to watch, it is certainly not fast. We find using two spoons alleviates this problem. One spoon is used by the parent for the feeding, and the second spoon is used to entertain the child.

A 6-month-old can also chew on what I call "too big foods." These are things like a toasted half of a bagel, a large carrot, a large piece of apple or Zwieback Teething Toast. These are food items a child can chew on and taste, but are "too big" to really eat. In our home, these are usually large pieces of what the other kids are eating. If we are having bagels for breakfast, then we will give the baby a bagel to chew on. At seven months, our eighth child loved green salads. Yes, despite a complete lack of teeth or any ability to eat it, she loved salad. If we failed to serve her a salad, she would cry and scream until we did. Once served, she would chew on every piece then spit it on the floor.

At six to seven months, we often begin fresh fruit offered in a mesh fruit feeder. These feeders are basically a mesh net attached to a plastic handle. Parents fill them with soft fresh fruit and children are able to safely self feed. We usually offer watermelon, cantaloupe, peaches or bananas. Bananas are the easiest as they are always available at the store. Unfortunately, they turn slimy and brown by the time clean up time comes.

At seven to eight months, children can begin the small pick up foods like Cheerios, puffs or peas. Finger snack foods are fun, but there is very little nutritional value in them. We like to look at them as more of an activity. Most 6-month-olds could eat them, but do not have the manual dexterity to pick them up. Children learn to use a pincer grasp (finger and thumb pinch) between six to nine months. Offering these types of foods should improve the child's fine motor pincer grasp.

 Start finger foods at seven to eight months.

At the Gordon house, 9-month-olds will often be offered thinly sliced turkey from the deli, cut up pieces of fruit (like quarters of a grape) and pieces of pasta. Really, whatever we are eating, we cut up into Cheerio size pieces. As children near nine months old, they often closely watch their parents eat. They begin to want to eat what you eat and when you're eating it. In this way, by nine months, most children are receiving solids three times a day. As I've previously stated, our youngest was one of our most aggressive eaters. When she was eight months old, for dinner she ate shredded grilled chicken, pieces of strawberries, baked potato and she chewed on a spinach salad. This is exactly what we all ate. When my wife attempted to spoon feed Stage 2 mixed vegetables, she refused. She turned her head and pushed the spoon away.

When should we start sippy cups?

At six months you can introduce sippy cups, fruit mesh feeders and "too big foods."

Parents can introduce sippy cups between six to nine months. They aren't easy, and your child may need some practice before mastering the ability to use a sippy cup. Frankly, I'm surprised by the amount of force required to drink from a "no-spill" sippy cup. You may have to try a variety of cups to get started - straw cups or cups that leak when upside down. Sometimes we have to pull the no-spill valves out for our children to begin to understand the concept. Juice boxes are a great way to teach a young child how to use a straw. Simply squeeze the sides to squirt a little juice in their mouths, and most children quickly understand the concept.

Food Irritants

Local reactions to foods are common in young children. It is impossible to know exactly what foods will upset an individual. I would not want to limit all of these foods, as most of them are the nutritious items that we want our children to eat. Let's just call this a list of foods to watch.

Foods which can cause skin irritation:
• Oranges, lemons, limes and grapefruit, including their juices
• Tomatoes and tomato products
• Blueberries, strawberries and raspberries
• Mangos, pineapple and cantaloupe.

These same food items will also cause contact irritant diaper rashes on the way out. One of our children loved orange juice as a toddler. Unfortunately, every time she had some, she would quickly get a diaper rash. We learned to decrease her orange juice intake and even apply preventative barrier diaper rash cream. These rashes were actually a motivating factor during her potty training days.

While not a *true* allergic reaction, these rashes can cause discomfort. They tend to occur in sensitive, fair skinned individuals. The reactions can be worse if the skin is already irritated (dry or chapped). As children get older, they are usually able to tolerate these foods.

If your child develops a facial or diaper rash after eating one of these foods, avoid feeding him the item for a couple weeks. When you do retry the irritant food, start with a small amount. Non-local swelling, changes in breathing or voice, hives or vomiting are all signs of a more serious allergic reaction.

Six Months Sleep

Waking at Night after Regularly Sleeping through the Night

Travel, illness and visitors are the three classic causes which disturb the sleep of families whose children have learned to sleep through the night. When your child wakes at night, you need to go to him. Assess the situation, but minimize your interaction. You don't want a few nights of waking to create a habit of waking.

You need to take care of him, but limit that care. If his pacifier has fallen on the floor, give it to him. If he is cold, turn up the heat. Only pick him up or feed him if absolutely necessary.

If your son wakes with a fever, give him either acetaminophen or ibuprofen and hold him. Ibuprofen is approved for children six months and older. The next night, if he is still sick, give him a dose of ibuprofen before bedtime. Ibuprofen (Motrin or Advil) is my recommended nighttime fever reducer, as it lasts for six to eight hours. Acetaminophen (Tylenol) only last four to six hours. More on acetaminophen and ibuprofen can be found on page 108.

One or two nights of wakings is common and not a problem. What we want to avoid is creating a habit.

Pacifier Causing Waking

Parent Question:

For the last month, our 6-month-old has been waking at night. We do not need to hold or feed her. She just wants the pacifier. I think she wakes up as soon as the pacifier falls out of her mouth. If we give her the pacifier once or twice at night, she sleeps at least eight hours. What should we do?

99

Overall, it sounds like you're really close to sleeping well. Try taking out her pacifier after she falls asleep. We want her to get used to sleeping without the pacifier in her mouth. This may take some time and persistence. Your other option is to place multiple pacifiers in her crib at night. This helps increase the odds of her finding a pacifier on her own. Hang in there; she is really close. Most children develop the coordination to replace their pacifiers between six to nine months.

If your child has failed to learn to sleep through the night, it may be time to "cry it out."

Crying it Out (over six months)

The term *crying it out* means different things to different people. Crying it out is an old-school, effective technique to teach children how to fall asleep on their own. It is stressful, however, for both child and parents and should only be a last resort. Unfortunately, crying it out is the only way to improve the sleep habits of some children. It is an appropriate technique for children six months and older.

There are three effective methods of crying it out distinguished by the frequency of "checking in:"

1) Never checking - Parent completes bedtime routine, closes the door and does not return.
2) Set interval checking - Parent completes bedtime routine and checks on child at consistent 15 or 20 minute intervals.
3) Increasing interval checking - Parent completes bedtime routine and checks on child at increasing intervals. Initially after 15 minutes, then after 20 minutes, then after 25 minutes and so forth. This method allows you to start with a time interval "right" for your baby.

If you check on your child, make it quick. Simply re-swaddle, reposition or offer a pacifier. Do not turn on the lights. Try not to make eye contact, and absolutely do not pick him up or feed him.

Generally, all three methods work well - as long as the parents strictly adhere to the rules. Before starting the "cry it out" method, all involved care givers must pick a method and agree to the plan. If you plan on "checking in" you must use a timer - as one minute often seems like 15 minutes when it is *your* baby crying.

Once you begin the cry it out method, you must not give up. You must stick to the plan. If you end up picking up or feeding your child, you will only encourage more crying in the future. Through giving in, you effectively reward the child's crying behavior. The lesson learned by the child is, "If I cry, I get what I want." Sure this applies to bedtime now, but soon it will also apply to lollipops and new toys. The next time you try to cry it out, your child will cry longer and more intensely. However, if you just can't take it and you give in one night, don't completely quit. Start again the next night. This is a huge challenge, but with great rewards for all.

You should not begin to let your child "cry it out" unless you are:
1) willing to let him cry all night and
2) believe that doing it is in your child's best interest.

Deciding to "cry it out" is often a last resort. Many families turn to it only after multiple attempts at sleep training have failed. I have worked with some families where one parent is "weak" and unable to listen to their child cry. Sometimes it is best for the "weaker" parent to get out of the house at bedtime. Go for a walk, visit friends or catch a movie.

During the initial two weeks, you may go to your child if he wakes up after he has already fallen asleep. After, he has learned to fall asleep on his own, most children will learn to put themselves back to sleep in the middle of the night.

If you do decide to let your child cry it out, realize that the first night will be horrible, but the fifth night will be worse. After two weeks, your child will learn to fall asleep on his own. Often, it is the same parents that dread crying it out that state they should have done it sooner.

Vomiters, Head Bangers and Breath Holders

> **Do not attempt to cry it out unless both parents are committed to a specific plan.**

Often, parents refuse to attempt crying it out, because their child vomits, bangs his head or holds his breath when upset. These issues are normal and very common. If you allow these behaviors to cause you to give up, then you will get more crying, head banging, vomiting and breath holding.

Some children will bang their heads on the crib enough to cause bruises. Given time, children will learn that this hurts and eventually will stop.

If the child vomits in his crib, I recommend you change the sheets and clean up after the child falls asleep. If your child is a regular vomitter, try making his bed using two sets of mattress pads and fitted sheets. After your child is asleep (and has vomited), simply removed the top set.

During my first weekend on call in private practice, I was contacted by an ER doctor from a small hospital. He was seeing one of our patients and wanted to admit the child for breath holding spells. After some discussion, the ER doctor began to see that we could not hospitalize this little boy until he grew old enough to not hold his breath when upset. The child had terrified the parents and even the ER doc by turning blue and passing out. Fortunately, the child did not need to be hospitalized. Unfortunately, the only cure is time and consistent discipline.

Crying it Out Not Working

Parent Question:

Our almost 8-month-old daughter wants me to hold her all the time and cannot self soothe. I can't walk out of the room for one minute even when I'm in eyesight; she wants me within arm's reach constantly. I've tried the cry it out method during playtimes throughout the day and at night in her crib, but she cries for three to four hours straight and I feel like it's not working for her. Are there some babies that CIO just doesn't work for? Do you have any advice? We are desperate! She's always been this way, and I'm afraid I've created a spoiled baby who can't self-soothe (according to family members).

It sounds like its time to hold and love your daughter. We have tried unsuccessfully at our home to use a playpen. Frankly, our kids cried every time we walked by. The crying made us (the parents), our baby and their siblings miserable.

We have found "crying it out" beneficial to teach children to fall asleep on their own, but I do not recommend it for other applications. Crying it out is emotionally exhausting for parents. I fear that by fighting the battle during the day and night, you are losing the war. Hold and love her during the day, and save your energy for improving her nighttime issues.

For her daytime anxiety, purchase a baby carrier or sling and strap her onto you. Give her the security she currently needs. It will be difficult for you to get your chores done, but it is more important that your daughter feels secure. This is a phase, and it will pass.

The nighttime is the bigger issue. It is essential that you teach her to sleep on her own at night. If you are trying to let her cry it out and then giving in to her, you are training her to cry.

Follow up one month later

She is doing much better. She now sleeps through the night a good 10 to 12 hours. The daytime crying is going better as well! I do think it was a phase like you said, and now that she's crawling and mobile, it helped a lot! She still cries and fusses when I'm out of eyesight for a few seconds, but it's much, much better. After I got your response and I held her and responded to her cries during the day, I feel like she didn't cry as much at night when we did CIO to conquer sleeping through the night.

Six-month-old Not Sleeping at Night

Parent Question:

My son is turning six months in a few days. He is not sleeping through the night. Right now, he sleeps from 7 p.m. to about 7 a.m. He has had a consistent bedtime routine since three months. Going to bed isn't the issue, it's staying asleep. He is placed in his crib awake and can put himself to sleep; however, when he wakes during the night, he will rarely go to sleep without being fed. He usually wakes twice to eat, and multiple other times where I give him his pacifier and then he falls back asleep.

While he is almost old enough to cry it out, I don't think you will need to. He seems really close. Eliminate the middle of the night feedings. He is dependent on these calories and will likely continue to wake up if these are continued. Offer the pacifier and any other forms of comfort first. Any shifting of these feedings toward waking hours should be seen as progress. Fewer ounces and moving a feeding later should lead to less caloric need and therefore less waking. How often does he eat during the day? He should be able to space out his daytime feeding to at least four hours. If he does not make it four hours between feeding, slowly space out the daytime feedings. See the section on Spacing it Out on page 67. You could try to wake and feed him prior to your bedtime. Many families have success with this technique. The pacifier may quickly become your best ally. Usually between six to eight months, children develop the ability to put a pacifier in their own mouths. Try placing multiple pacifiers in his bed. With a little improved fine motor coordination, he may soon be calming himself down. While 7 p.m. to 7 a.m. sounds good, the goal is six to eight hours of sleep without the need for parental invention. Focus on a few quality hours, and he should extend his nighttime sleep with time.

Follow up two months later

He is now almost nine months and sleeping great!!! He usually sleeps from 7 p.m. to 5 or 5:30 a.m. and then has a bottle and goes back down until about 7 a.m.

Moving Bedtime

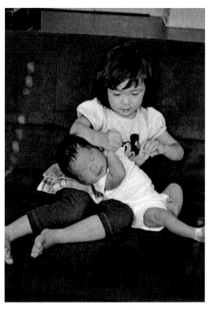

Parent Question:

I just wanted to thank you for posting information on your website about putting newborns to sleep. We put our daughter down each night around 10:30 p.m. with the same routine (bath, dress, bottle, rocking baby to sleep), which worked well for the first six months. When she turned six months, we decided that it was time for her to learn how to fall asleep on her own. We follow a similar routine at an earlier time 8:30 to 9 p.m. (bath, dress, bottle, reading, prayer). The first night was the most difficult,
because she cried for half an hour. We forced ourselves not to console her. She began to settle down in the subsequent nights. Now that we've been putting her down this way for about two weeks, she seems to understand that she is responsible for falling asleep on her own. She tosses and turns for 15 to 20 minutes, but she falls asleep on her own. Would you recommend putting her down at an even earlier time? Like 7-7:30 p.m.?

I'm glad to hear that she is sleeping well and has learned to settle herself down at night. How long is she sleeping? I would try putting her to sleep earlier if she is consistently sleeping later than you want her to.

We moved our children to 7 or 8 p.m. bedtimes when they either:
1) became physically tired from learning to crawl or spending time outside and/or
2) dropped down from three to two naps a day.
There is really no right or wrong answer in this situation. There is little harm in trying an early bedtime and seeing how she sleeps.

Follow up two months later

Good news! We moved her bedtime up to 7 p.m. It was working, and then the time change happened and that really got her there. Initially we made progress through gradually making her bedtime earlier. We were really helped by the time change. Suddenly 8 p.m. was 7 p.m. The combination of gradually moving the bedtime earlier and a time change helped us move her bedtime two hours earlier.

Follow up two years later

As for a follow up, we're actually right in the middle of applying the sleep training principles on her new sister. We aren't changing anything from the way that we handled our first daughter's sleep training, since it was successful the first time around. Just like with her older sister, our new baby slept through the night at two months old. We had some setback last week when she got sick, but she's making progress toward sleeping through the night again.

We can't thank you enough for stressing the importance of sleep training. My parents are thrilled that our older daughter pretty much puts herself down at night when she stays over at their house. She tells them when she's tired and insists on her routine (bath, milk, tooth brushing, book, song, prayer and sleep). When they forget to pray, she makes sure that they do it. A 2.5-year-old who can't miss a day without prayer? What parent wouldn't want one of those!

Still Not Sleeping

Prior to six months old, I recommend the simple methods described in the first part of this book. Families who embrace these concepts are frequently impressed by the simplicity and effectiveness of this method.

Unfortunately, some children have still failed to master sleeping through the night by six months old. Sadly, many parents only begin thinking about their child's sleep habits after they realize that their friends' babies are already sleeping.

Reasons for not sleeping through the night seem to fall into two basic categories:

1) Childhood illness - preemies, chronic infections, severe reflux/fussy babies, growth problems

2) Parental - Inability to provide consistent environment, lack of knowledge of sleep training methods, failure to employ sleep methods.

I hear about sleep problems every day in my office. Often, the stories are the same, "It seemed easier just to feed him and go back to bed," or "When he cries, I simply bring him to our bed." These responses make me think of the story of a young sailor with a leaky boat.

While sailing one day, a young sailor discovered a leak in his boat. He knew to repair it right, he would have to pull it onto land and to properly patch the hull. To this beginner, all this work seemed unnecessarily hard. He continued to sail and bail out the water when needed. Initially, it

seemed easier to bail out a few cups of water every day. As the leak slowly grew, the bailing became a greater burden.
Eventually, the sailor became tired of bailing and pulled the boat out. He had to fix the initial crack, plus repair the damage that occurred from sailing a damaged boat.

The point of my story is both that it is easier to fix issues before they become chronic, and that months of bad sleep habits are hard to repair - but it can be done. It takes commitment, a specific plan and hard work.

At this point you still need to:

1) Establish a bright, stimulating day and a dark, boring night
2) Have a strict bedtime routine
3) Space out feedings to every 3.5 to 4 hours
4) Teach them to fall asleep on their own. Usually "crying it out" is the best method.

There are many experts who have their own "sleep recipes." If my methods do not sound like the right techniques for your family, then research other sleep training books, and find one that suits your lifestyle. Read other books, and talk to more parents. Work with your spouse (or family) to come up with a plan that everyone can agree on. Often, dads want to "cry it out" and mothers are unwilling or unable. It won't work unless you are both on board. Many relationships get unnecessarily strained over this issue. It's hard to be cordial when you are physically exhausted and emotionally overwhelmed.

Acetaminophen and Ibuprofen

Parent Question:

What dose of Tylenol (acetaminophen) and Motrin/Advil (ibuprofen) do you use for your family? Do you give both together? At what temperature do you give these fever reducers?

 Ibuprofen may be given to children six months and older.

I agree with the rule "treat the child, not the fever." If one of our children has a 102°F fever and is running around (acting well), then I would not give a fever reducer (acetaminophen/ibuprofen). If one our children has a 101°F fever and is crying and uncomfortable, I would give either acetaminophen or ibuprofen.

I personally think ibuprofen works better, but we keep both medications in our home. Ibuprofen seems to work quicker and last longer. For this reason, I try to make the last dose before bedtime an ibuprofen dose. Our children often develop a fever around dinnertime. When they do, we give acetaminophen then, so we can give an ibuprofen dose a couple of hours later.

We will give both medications at the same time or a few hours apart - as long as acetaminophen doses are six hours from the last acetaminophen dose and ibuprofen doses are six hours from the last ibuprofen dose.

We do use both acetaminophen and ibuprofen in our home. I usually calculate doses based on our child's weight. We do not use acetaminophen until our children are at least two months old. I use the standard 15 mg of acetaminophen per kg dose for our children. I dose acetaminophen every six hours. We usually give their first dose at two months prior to their 2-

month vaccinations. Ibuprofen (Motrin / Advil) is not approved for use in children under six months old. Ibuprofen is dosed at 5 to 10 mg per kg every six hours.

I recommend that parents purchase only the 160 mg/5 ml Tylenol (acetaminophen) and the 100 mg/5 ml ibuprofen. These two medication concentrations can be dosed the exact same. This system avoids confusion and therefore prevents inaccurate dosing. Using these doses and concentrations, a table can be derived:

Weight lbs(kg)	Acetaminophen 160mg/5ml	Ibuprofen 100mg/5ml
5 to 11 lbs (2 to 5 kg)	1 ml	
11 to 15 lbs (5 to 7 kg)	2 ml	
15 to 20 lbs (7 to 9 kg)	3 ml	3 ml
20 to 23 lbs (9 to 11 kg)	4 ml	4 ml
23 to 28 lbs (11 to 13 kg)	5 ml	5 ml
28 to 33 lbs (13 to 15 kg)	6 ml	6 ml
33 to 38 lbs (15 to 17 kg)	7 ml	7 ml
38 to 42 lbs (17 to 19 kg)	8 ml	8 ml
42 to 47 lbs (19 to 21 kg)	9 ml	9 ml
47 lbs (21kg)	10 ml	10 ml

gregorygordonmd.com

Gregory Gordon, MD

Nine Months

During my residency, I was given one full weekend off each month. As a father of two children with a wife staying at home, I was always looking for opportunities to earn some extra cash. I ended up moonlighting on my weekends off. When it was announced that a rural Alabama hospital was looking for pediatric coverage on weekends, I signed up. I would take call at the

Children's Hospital in Birmingham on Thursday nights. After rounding and finishing up my residency work on Friday, our family would head to Sylacauga, Alabama to begin my second job providing pediatric coverage for Coosa Valley Medical Center. Looking back, this opportunity forced me to learn and taught me to make decisions.

As we became more familiar with the town of Sylacauga, we developed a weekend routine. Every weekend, we stayed in the same room of the Jameson Inn. After working in the mornings, our family would spend three to four hours at a small park. We ate breakfast at the inn and went out for lunches and dinners. Every Friday night, we ate at our favorite Mexican restaurant.

Maggie and I grew to love these weekends. I enjoyed the responsibility and decision making at the hospital. Maggie and I both enjoyed the time we spent with our kids. We looked at these weekends more as a vacation. In our real lives, we rarely ate at a restaurant or spent seemingly endless hours at a park.

We have many fond memories of these weekends. We both remember habitually ordering a bowl of guacamole for our son Isaac (when six to nine months old) on our Friday Mexican restaurant trips. It began after we forgot to pack jarred food. We improvised by ordering a bowl of guac. Isaac loved it, and we felt good about feeding it to him.

Nine Months Feeding

Best Eaters

 Nine to 10-month-olds are the "best eaters."

Typically, 9 to 10-month-olds are described as the "best eaters" by adults impressed with the variety and quantity of food ingested. Nine-month-olds often eat more than their 3-year-old siblings. At check ups, parents often ask, "How much food is too much?" Grandmothers love to feed children this age as there seems no limit to the variety and quantity of foods. Unfortunately, most of these "good eaters" gradually get pickier until they reach their pickiest around 18 months old. Classically, toddlers between 18 to 36 months run around busy all day, but only eat infrequent, small quantities of food.

As children become more efficient at eating solid foods, their drive for breast milk or formula begins to wane. Children usually drink 25 to 35 ounces of milk each day between four to nine months. After nine months, children slowly begin to drink less. By twelve months, children only need 10 to 12 ounces of whole milk each day.

When can we start Stage 3 foods?

Children are usually ready for Stage 3 foods around eight to nine months old. Stage 3 foods contain grains of rice, kernels of corn and whole peas. When children are ready for Stage 3 jarred foods, they are ready for many table foods. We rarely feed our children Stage 3 foods. We prefer to feed

111

them table foods along with the rest of the family. In our home, Stage 3 jar foods are reserved for travel or other times when convenience is a priority. Changing to table foods at this age seems natural. At this age, our children preferred to eat the items they saw the rest of the family eating.

Transition from Baby Food to Table Food

Parent Question:

I want to start weaning my 10-month-old off baby jar food and onto real, finger foods, but I haven't the slightest idea how much and what kind of food to give for breakfast, lunch, and dinner.

There is great variation in what 10-month-olds can eat. In the Gordon home, we have had a son who ate pizza (cut up into pieces) at seven months and a daughter who struggled to wean off pureed food at one year.

We like to move quickly through baby foods as solid foods are easier and, we think, better for the child. I would much rather feed my child a fresh banana over one that has been sitting in a jar for six months. Our youngest was off jar food at nine months old.

What can your 10-month-old currently eat? If he only recently began Stage 1 jar foods, then he may only be ready for Stage 2 foods and solids like mashed potatoes or fruit in a mesh feeder. If he is taking Stage 2 foods well or some Stage 3 foods, then he should be ready for some table foods.

Most 10-month-olds want to eat what you are eating. If you are having lasagna, salad and garlic toast for dinner, then try cut up lasagna and garlic toast. It is wise to offer him some salad, but he will not be able to eat lettuce yet. If you are having grilled chicken for dinner, I doubt he is ready to eat grilled chicken chunks, but should be able to eat the baked beans, fruit salad and baked potato that go with it.

 Table foods can be started after eight months.

Other foods you can feed include:

Canned veggies like peas or green beans (low sodium), steamed broccoli in small pieces, halves of grapes, all kinds of cooked beans, thinly sliced turkey from the deli, slices of cheese, yogurt, Nutrigrain bars and pancakes.

The challenge at this age is quality. You will really have to make an effort to feed fruits and veggies. Typical serving sizes at this age are one to two tablespoons. Examples of this small serving size includes: two broccoli florets or twenty peas. One tablespoon is surprisingly little but important for the development of good habits. Always serve the veggie first, when possible in the light of the ultimate goal of a healthy diet. Most 10-month-olds are great eaters and will eat well when offered food.

What does your child actually eat?

Our eighth child was one of our more aggressive eaters and seemed to want to keep up with her older siblings. Over 48 hours one weekend when she was 9 months old, she ate:

Breakfast: pancakes, an omelet (including diced tomatoes, onions, yellow pepper and cheese) and home fries

Fruits: banana, watermelon, cantaloupe, honeydew, blueberries, strawberries and mango salsa (diced mango and avocado)

Dinner/Lunches: broken pieces of hamburger, penne pasta, steamed broccoli, a green salad, angel hair pasta with marinara, shredded chicken, cooked peas, cooked corn, black beans, cooked spinach and a baked potato.

We feed her 98% of what we eat. The hamburger is broken up and the chicken is shredded. The peas, corn and beans are often swallowed whole or partially smashed. She self feeds and makes a huge mess. Our dog likes to hang out under her chair. The only thing I can think of that we didn't feed her (that we ate) this weekend was popcorn.

Teeth play almost no role in the introduction of solid foods. Our daughter ate all of the above with essentially no teeth. New parents often falsely believe teeth are necessary to start solid foods. The first eight teeth that erupt in most children are their incisors. The incisors are the front flat teeth used

> **The average child gets his first tooth (a lower incisor) between six to eight months.**

to bite off pieces of food. They are not involved in chewing. The first chewing teeth to erupt are their 15-month-old molars. I don't know of any feeding recommendations that wait for a full set of molars to start table foods.

Can my 9-month-old baby eat eggs?

Parent Question:

I noticed on your website you feed your 9-month-olds eggs. Is that safe with regards to food allergies?

We feed our children eggs beginning at nine months. Scrambled eggs are a great protein source that beginner table food eaters enjoy. They are soft, easy to self feed and do not pose a choking risk. In the past decade, many feeding experts have recommended waiting to introduce eggs and other common food allergens. Doctors recommended feeding egg yolks at twelve months and egg whites at two years. Egg whites were delayed as they are one of the six most common food allergens. This recommendation was based partly on some early research, but more on the opinions of experts who proposed the idea that early introduction of foods created food allergies.

More recent research has challenged this once commonly held hypothesis. Since 2007, researchers have published numerous studies that directly contradicted these previously widely-held beliefs. Their research indicated that the best treatment for egg allergies might just be eggs themselves.

Recently, the AAP asked a group of experts to examine this controversy. In 2008, the AAP updated its recommendations after reviewing the current evidence on this issue. The AAP Committee on Nutrition and Section on Allergy and Immunology concluded there was no relationship between the timing of introductions of solid food and the development of allergic conditions.

When can I give cow's milk to my baby?

The AAP recommendation to start whole milk at one year is a rounded age. Unlike formula, cow's milk should only be a portion of the child's diet. Cow's milk is not complete nutrition (except for calves).

 Cow's milk is safe for most 10 to 11-month-old children.

At one year, we work toward serving milk only at meals. Whole milk should not be given in bottles. Serving cow's milk in bottles only delays a transition that ultimately needs to happen.

Importantly, cow's milk should be only a portion of a 1-year-old's diet. Cow's milk, unlike infant formula, is not complete nutrition. Some 1-year-olds will drink milk instead of eating other foods.

Children who drink milk instead of solids can develop iron deficiency anemia. Children only need 10 to 12 ounces of whole milk a day between one to two years of age. A 1-year-old that is eating good quantities of a variety of solid foods can tolerate more than 12 ounces daily. It is the children who drink 30 to 40 ounces of milk and refuse solids that develop health issues.

Don't expect your son to hear any better than his father.

Gordonian Wisdom

Should we gradually mix the milk into the formula?

At one year of age, children should be transitioned off formula onto whole milk. One-year-olds need a diet that remains high in fat for continued brain development. Children continue to myelinate (cover with a fatty insulation) brain and nerve cells until two years old.

When transitioning to cow's milk from formula, I recommend a simple, abrupt transition. While some people gradually mix formula and cow's milk, I find this confuses the issue with no apparent benefit. Parents and some experts feel that by mixing the cow's milk with the formula, it provides a gentler transition. For example, proponents of mixing may recommend a week drinking 75% formula with 25% cow's milk. These schedules sound scientific, but I can find no scientific basis for them. Mixing seems like excess effort with no benefit. Mixing also confuses the question of tolerance. During a prolonged several week introduction, children are bound to be fussy or become sick. This raises the question, "Are the symptoms because of the cow's milk?" In our home, we keep it simple and offer them a sippy cup with three to four ounces of whole milk around 12 months of age. Our first seven have enjoyed and tolerated the cow's milk without the need for a complicated, prolonged transition.

What about spices in table foods?

Most children tolerate the spices in their parents' foods. With our oldest, we worried about and took great care not to expose her to anything too spicy. We did not allow her to taste salsas and even prepared some dishes separately. A few children later, (and a lot busier), we simply give our children the same foods we eat. Only rarely, have they cried, "It's too spicy." Maggie and I both will add hot sauce to our chili. Often, our children will ask to do the same. We allow them to add Tabasco or other seasoning but try to limit the amount. A few times, our children have ignored our hot sauce warnings. The consequence of these poor listening incidences are simple, natural consequences. Red eyes and a few tears often remind them to listen better and limit their own spices.

When my son, Isaac, was six years old, he played on a soccer team at the local YMCA. After the game, Isaac was invited to join another family for lunch at a nearby restaurant. Both Isaac and his friend ordered chicken wings. Isaac ordered his wings "hot." He persisted with his order despite questioning from the family and warning by the waitress. Fortunately, Isaac loves spicy, and he amazed our friends by eating all his wings.

Nine Months Discipline

Discipline is the hardest part of parenting. While immensely important, good discipline often seems to contradict parental instincts. After a long day of work, few parents want to place their child in time out.

This section is on starting discipline. Often the parents of 9-month-olds are surprised when I bring up the subject. It is placed in the Nine Months Chapter as I want parents to discuss and think about discipline before bad habits develop. This is not intended as a complete book of instructions, but hopefully a solid foundation to build upon.

Why Discipline?

Discipline is important. When you walk into that first kindergarten teacher conference, what do you want to hear? You want to hear that your child is well behaved, smart and a joy to have in class. If he cannot behave at home, he will not behave at school.

Early discipline is critical to early schooling success. If your child is poorly behaved, do you think he will learn as much? Will he be encouraged by his teachers? Will he feel good about himself?

Parenthood is God's way of humbling us.

Gordonian Wisdom

As a young parent, I once had an attending physician tell me he and his wife *never* disciplined their children. Since he was my boss, I merely smiled and nodded. Really? Did they let their children stick things in electrical outlets? Was TV time unlimited? Did they eat whatever, whenever they wanted? I chuckle as I visualize *Lord of the Flies* in a suburban home.

What is Discipline?

Discipline is how we teach our children safety, social expectations and limits. We hope as parents, that by consistently placing our toddler in time out, he will learn not to bite his friend. By consistently providing negative consequences for undesired behavior, our children should learn appropriate behaviors. In time, growing children should learn to discipline themselves. Hopefully, they will learn to limit their play time to finish their research paper.

When to Start Discipline

 Discipline should start around nine months.

Discipline should begin shortly after a child begins to crawl. As children begin to move around the home, they gain access to outlets, toilets, stairs and other hazards. Discipline should start with safety. Childproofing the home only goes so far.

What are you going to do when he uses a toy to pry off a protective outlet cover? Or climbs on top of the refrigerator? How about pulling a friends hair?

Eventually, you are going to have to start discipline. If you start discipline from the beginning, it is easier than playing catch up after your child is "out of control."

Don't Say "No" Unless You have a Plan

Begin by holding your tongue. As much as possible, avoid the "no" word (or any other negative words or warning sounds). When you use the word "no," it should have meaning. Your child should learn that the word "no" means "if you continue to do that, there will be consequences." Be as consistent as possible. Only say "no" when you are prepared to act.

I often hear all about toddlers who are "out of control." "He won't listen to me." If you tell your child "no" and there are no consequences, you are teaching your child to ignore your instructions. In reality, all parents (including myself) fail to discipline at times when we should. These inconsistencies are poor parenting moments, but not something to fret. Recognize these moments and continue with resolve to be more consistent in the future. When children are provided with well defined limits and clear rules, they will thrive.

Start with Distraction and Redirecting

Distraction and redirecting should be frequently used techniques in this early period only. If your 9-month-old son gets into the dog's food, pick him up (remove the food from his mouth), relocate him and offer him a toy.

Distraction and redirecting are not effective long term techniques. As children get smarter, these techniques simply do not work. Eventually, your son will persistently crawl back to the dog food. What are you going to do then?

 Distraction and redirection are the best initial discipline techniques.

Start by Developing a Plan

When our first child learned to climb and stand on our coffee table, we knew we had to begin discipline. The table had four sharp corners, she wasn't very coordinated and we were unwilling to get rid of our furniture. We needed a plan.

She would crawl over to the coffee table and put one knee up. We would call her name and say, "no." She would look at us, smile and proceed to climb on the coffee table. Clearly, our sweet, innocent, perfect child heard us and clearly, she was disobeying!

Maggie and I sat down and agreed we needed a plan of action for discipline. We both agreed that "time out" was a great place to start. With a unified, consistent plan, we were able to break this dangerous habit and teach her the concept of discipline.

Start "time out" between ten to twelve months.

The next time she crawled over to the coffee table, we said, "no." She smiled and continued to climb. We calmly said, "time out," picked her up and placed her in a play pen with no toys. In a few days, she understood "time out" and that climbing on the coffee table was not allowed.

Success came in stages. First, she learned to cry when we said, "time out." She then responded to the word "no" and crawled away from the table. Finally, she put her knee up on the table and decided not to climb. Our plan had worked! She learned not to climb on the coffee table. She also learned the concepts of "no" and "time out."

When discussing time out with new families, I recommend starting with one major safety problem. For us it was climbing on the coffee table. Use the singular issue to establish the concept of discipline. After the child learns about "no" and "time out," these concepts can be applied to other issues.

It all sounds so easy - it was not. This was harder to do with our first child. We were less confident parents. It's hard to hear your child cry and call out "Mama" or "Dada" because *you* put him in time out. After seeing the fruits of consistent time out, discipline became easier.

A few notes:

Discipline your child because you love your child.

1) Have a plan; it will help you stay calm.

2) When you say, "no," say it clearly and only once, but do not yell (not unless you want to yell for the next 18 years).

3) When you pick up your toddler to put him in time out, pick him up so he is facing away from you (so that you are looking at his back). Only use this unique hold when you are putting your child in timeout. It helps link the child's poor behavior with his discipline.

4) They should not be able to get out of "time out" (we used either a pack-n-play or the child's crib). Experts often discourage the use of the child's crib, but it has not been a problem in our home. Our children quickly learned the difference between being placed in time out and being placed in bed for sleep. The backwards "time out" hold and their bedtime routine make the difference clear.

5) While they are in "time out," you should completely ignore them. I often find that parents talk to their children or bring them toys while their kids are in "time out." You want them not to like it, and you need time to calm down.

Everything in moderation, except humor.

Gordonian Wisdom

6) You should put a toddler in time out long enough for him to stop crying. As children get older, you can use the one minute per year of age rule.

7) All of their caretakers need to be on board with the plan and be consistent.

8) When you are out of the house and they misbehave, use his stroller or car seat as his "time out" place.

9) When first implementing "time out," work with one major issue. During these early days, use distraction and redirection to deal with all the other issues.

10) When deciding on what behavior to address, first choose one that is:
    a) Repetitive and occurs multiple times each day
    b) Where the difference between good behavior and the undesired behavior is clearly defined. Climbing on a coffee table worked well because she was clearly either on the floor or on top of a table. Beginning "time out" to address screaming is much harder to define. Was it a scream? Should we put him

in "time out" for a scream when he fell and was injured? Was that scream loud enough to warrant a "time out?"

"I'm not ready to discipline"

Often, parents tell me they are not ready to start discipline. Unfortunately, most parents do not have a choice. Early discipline should focus on safety issues. Frankly, I'm not ready to have a teenage driver. It's really scary, but she needs to learn this life skill.

If your child is just innately "good," you can wait. Keep your eyes open. Consider the need for distraction and redirection as warning signs that your child will soon test you. If you find yourself telling your child "no," but have no plan if they fail to listen, you are in trouble.

Telling your child "no" and shouting is discipline. It is just bad discipline. You need to have a consistent, reasonable plan that allows discipline without raising your voice and a constant battle.

Parents who shy away from a discipline plan are failing to instruct and teach their children.

What are your options when your child repetitively sticks things in an outlet?

1) You could scream and shout "no." But what if that doesn't stop him?

2) You could give your child a snack every time. Effectively encouraging them by teaching your child that sticking things in an outlet gets him cookies and juice.

3) You could have a consistent plan for "time out."

Please Don't Count

I see all forms of discipline in my office. The least effective is 1,2,3 discipline. This is the idea that counting gives the child chances to listen. What it teaches children is they don't have to listen until Mom gets to three (and often three-and-a-half). Say it once, say it calmly and then act confidently.

Imagine your 3-year-old riding his bike in the road. You don't have time to count; he just needs to get out of the street quickly.

Gordon Discipline Mantra

The following is a collection of some of the discipline sayings Maggie and I repeat to ourselves and each other:

1) **Tell the truth even when it hurts.** Our hope is that by being honest about little things when the child is young, we will establish a foundation of honesty that will pay off when the child is older. Examples of little lies, "Mommy doesn't have any more money to buy you candy." It is much better to tell the child the truth, "I do not want to buy you any more candy as it is not good for you." This honesty should be age appropriate. There is little benefit in explaining the "birds and bees" to a 3-year-old when she asks, "Where do babies come from?"

2) **When you are struggling with your toddler, ask yourself, "What am I teaching my child?"** Often, parents realize they are the basis for the problem. With our first child, we brought a lollipop to church to pacify her during the service. When she made noise we gave it to her. The idea was to keep her quiet during the service. Unfortunately, she

is smart and quickly learned the lesson we were teaching: scream at church and you will get candy.

> ## We like to enroll our children in swim lessons between 9 to 12 months old.

3) **When discipline is "black and white" you must act.** By "black and white," we mean when the child knows he is doing the wrong thing, and he understands the consequences. There are a lot of times, as a parent, where the situation is unclear, and you do not know if you should discipline your child. As parents, we often pass up discipline opportunities because we are too busy, or frankly, don't like to punish our children. When the situation is clear (it is black and white), you must follow through with discipline.

4) **Train your children to answer when spoken to.** A simple "Yes, Mom" or "Yes, Ma'am" works well. By responding, the child acknowledges he heard and is beginning the first step of obedience. If a child does not respond when clearly addressed, send him to "time out." This is still an area we struggle with in our home, as this is an ongoing issue. After a "time out," we will call our son over to discuss the "time out." "Jimmy, come here." We expect Jimmy to say, "Yes, Dad" and walk directly to us. If he does not do both, I send him back to time out and try again in a little bit. During the "time out discussion," we ask him two questions, "Do you know why I had to send you to time out?" and "Can you do better?" They need to answer both or go back for more "time out."

5) **Use the golden rule.** Treat others as you would want to be treated. Sure, this applies from brother to sister, but it also applies between parent to child. We often remind our children of this rule, but we need to remind ourselves of it more often.

Please do not read this section on discipline and think we are perfect. Our kids are not perfect, they come from imperfect parents. Maggie and I constantly talk about ways to become better parents. All parents should have this discussion and be open to criticism.

It's tough to listen to your spouse tell you that you need to work on your parenting or discipline techniques, but it is important. With our first toddler, I would often finish discipline statements with "OK?" "You don't pull the dog's tail, OK?" For me, this ending seemed softer and less paternal. Maggie rightly corrected this habit and asked "Are you asking her permission?" When analyzing these statements, I realized Maggie was right. It was clearer to drop the "OK?" I really did not want her to answer that it wasn't "OK."

Parenting is a learning process. No matter how hard you try, you will make mistakes. Maggie and I have made plenty of mistakes over the years. After eight children, we feel pretty good about some of the basics.

New parents often see our family at a restaurant or sit through a church service and think we are perfect parents. We definitely are not perfect, but we are practiced. We yell, get upset and say things we should not. Maggie and I are keenly aware of many of our shortcomings. It is important to acknowledge your flaws and work on them. Apologize to your children (and spouse) when necessary. Let them know you love them, want the best for them and that you will try to do better. Then, very importantly, forgive yourself so you have the energy and resolve to face the next day renewed and bring up your children in love.

Twelve Months

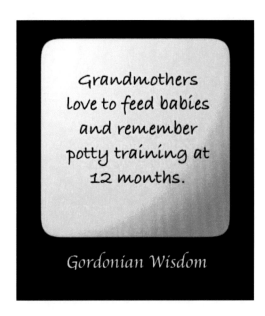

Grandmothers
love to feed babies
and remember
potty training at
12 months.

Gordonian Wisdom

Four days after our oldest daughter was born, our neighbors had a little boy. This little boy was our daughter's first "friend." While we were nervous and excited, his experienced parents were calm and confident. We celebrated many milestones and events together.

When the babies turned one, we hosted a combined birthday party complete with friends of both families, the whole neighborhood and distant relatives. We stressed about the details, ordered cakes from a specialty bakery and cleaned our house from top to bottom. Neither 1-year-old appreciated our effort, and both children fell asleep during the party. The party was more about celebrating our first year of parenting and love for our children.

Certain milestones seem more significant. Turning "One year old" always impresses me. As the age approached I often said, "I can't believe she is one." In my mind, "one" means the end of being "a baby" and the beginning of childhood. Babies need to be held, swaddled and burped. One-year-olds walk, talk and get into trouble.

Gregory Gordon, MD

Twelve Months Feeding

Twelve months is a time of feeding transition. Parents should stop baby food, formula and bottles. Children should be fed whole milk and the same healthy "table foods" as their parents. Between 12 to 24 months, parents should serve toddlers a relatively high fat diet. Including fat sources like whole milk, cheeses, yogurt, avocado and meats. This high fat diet is necessary to promote healthy brain development.

By 12 months, parents often notice a decline in their child's appetite. Typically, 9- to 10-month-olds are described as the "best eaters." At 9 to 10 months, parents often ask questions like, "Is it OK to keep feeding him?" and "When should we stop feeding her?" After this "peak," children generally become pickier. This is a gradual process. Children seem their "pickiest" between 18 and 36 months old. This pattern held true in our home, as most of our children's appetites decreased as toddlers.

In general, 12-month-olds should be eating the same table foods that their parents eat. In our home, breakfast and lunch tend to be "flexible meals." Meaning we are either having cereal or bagels for breakfast today. During the school year, our high school children eat before our younger children are even awake. When the meal plan is flexible, children should be offered a choice. Healthy parts of our meals are often mandatory. At lunch, my children may get to choose the type of sandwich they are served, but the cut up melon is part of all our meals.

Dinner is a family event in our home. At dinner, we say grace, talk and share the same meal together. The TV is off, and no phones or toys are allowed. It is often loud and interrupted by milk spills or someone racing off to an activity. It is imperfect, but we love it. All children, including 12-month-olds, are expected to follow the same rules. Twelve-month-olds should be securely strapped into a chair, served the same food, be required to sit for the entire meal and not have toys during meals. By raising children with these rules, they accept them. Parents and siblings should set a good example by eating a healthy diet.

In practice, I often find mothers that become short order cooks. They make one meal for the parents, and individual meals for each of their children. Children are often fed their favorite foods repetitively. Parents often do this because "he won't eat what we eat," or "I feed him what I know he will eat." Parents do this out of love and often fail to see the harm they are doing. One 2.5-year-old in my practice had been fed McDonald's chicken nuggets for breakfast, lunch and dinner for over a year! His mother went to McDonald's once or twice every day to support his habit. She knew that his diet was devoid of most nutrients, but she continued out of fear of him crying. His crying fits were made worse by months of enabling bad habits.

When Our Toddlers Cry or Persistently Misbehave at Meals

When toddlers persistently cry at meal times, use time out. Children in high chairs (with wheels) can simply be rolled into another room until they calm down. Children in clip on or other stationary chairs must be removed from their chair and placed in time out. Only once they are done crying can they return to the meal.

Parents will often try to appease crying young children with toys, movies or favorite foods. These gifts serve as a reward. Through rewarding undesirable behavior, these parents encourage their children to cry and misbehave during meals.

We have all seen these families at restaurants. These are the families whose toddlers are watching movies on an iPad while the older children and adults play on their phones. These families are missing out on precious family time. They are failing to develop the bonding and communication skills necessary for a strong family.

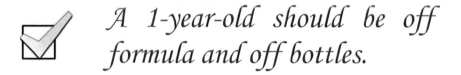 *A 1-year-old should be off formula and off bottles.*

Milk at Twelve Months

A 1-year-old should be off formula and off bottles. Prolonged use of bottles causes cavities and increases a child's risk of ear infections. The average 9-month-old needs about thirty ounces of formula a day. In contrast, the average 1-year-old needs only 10 to 12 ounces of whole milk a day.

Importantly, by 12 to 15 months, milk should only be a small portion of a child's diet. Children should drink mostly water, 10 to 12 ounces of milk and a small amount of juice (if desired). An individual should not be heavily dependent on any single food item. Formula is designed to be complete nutrition, milk is not. Occasionally, I will find a toddler who drinks in excess of 40 ounces each day. Most of these children love milk and quit eating solid foods as they do not need the calories. Children who exclusively drink cow's milk will eventually become iron deficient.

During my residency, I admitted a "cow's milk loving" seriously iron deficient toddler. This 2-year-old drank over 50 ounces a day in bottles. His iron levels had fallen to such a critical level that we had to put him in the hospital. He was particularly grumpy and fought the children's hospital staff. After presenting the case to our attending, she asked, "How was his behavior?" In her words, "These milk dependent, iron deficient children are mean." After he was stabilized, he was discharged home. A month later, he presented to our clinic for follow up. His iron levels were improving, and his parents happily reported a massive improvement in his personality.

When children drink too much milk, the easiest way to restrict their intake is to change how they drink their milk. Meaning, switch bottle drinkers to sippy cups and sippy cup drinkers to open cups.

While some children drink excess milk, others refuse milk. Milk refusal should be addressed like refusal of any other healthy food - by setting a good example, persistence and time. Children who refuse milk should be served milk as their only beverage option at lunch and dinner. Parents should set a good example by drinking milk, too. One of my daughters refused to drink milk at 12 months. We persistently served her milk at meals and drank milk in front of her. Finally after six months, she began to drink milk as well.

There are many types of milk available for toddlers: cow's milk, soy milk, goat's milk, almond milk, rice milk and even toddler formulas. It is impossible to say which milk is "best," as each type has its own advocates and nutrient benefits. In our home, toddlers drink whole cow's milk. It is not that I believe cow's milk is superior to other types of milk, but it is certainly not worse. In the United States, cow's milk is clearly the standard by which all other milks are measured. A toddler's milk should be a good source of fat, calcium and vitamin D.

Peanut Butter

Parent Question:

When is a good time to introduce peanut butter into a child's diet? Everything I've read is so conflicting.

In the last five years, there have been dramatic changes in recommendations on starting solid foods. Once strict guidelines with threatening warnings have now been replaced by loose evidence-based guidelines. This whirlwind change has lead to continued confusion on this issue.

When parents used to ask me, "When can we feed our baby peanut butter?" I use to ask, "Are you asking me or the American Academy of Pediatrics?" I would then explain the old AAP recommendation to wait until three years old and also explain my disagreement with that recommendation. Fortunately, times have changed and now I agree with the current recommendations.

Both the AAP and the American Academy of Asthma Allergy and Immunology (AAAAI) now feel peanut butter and other major food allergens are safe after four to six months.

> *"Although solid foods should not be introduced before four to six months of age, there is no current convincing evidence that delaying their introduction beyond this period has a significant protective effect on the development of atopic* (allergic) *disease regardless of whether infants are fed cow milk protein formula or human milk. This includes delaying the introduction of foods that are considered to be highly allergic, such as fish, eggs, and foods containing peanut protein."*
> *American Academy of Pediatrics website www.aap.org*

> The American Academy of Asthma Allergy and Immunology currently states: *"The introduction of solid foods should not be delayed beyond four to six months of age. Delaying the introduction of potentially allergenic foods, even in infants at risk for food allergy, has not been clearly shown to be beneficial."*
> *The American Academy of Allergy, Asthma and Immunology website www.aaaai.org*

Not only is there a lack of evidence that waiting to introduce peanut butter is beneficial, there is now evidence that early introduction is best. In 2009, Drs. Faith Huang and Anna Nowak-Wegrzyn published research titled "Early Consumption of Peanuts in Infancy Is Associated with a Low Prevalence of Peanut Allergy." Their paper showed that early introduction and frequent exposure to peanut products actually reduces a child's risk of acquiring food allergies. They found a tenfold greater risk of peanut allergy in children who were exposed to peanuts later in life.

Children get louder as they get older.

Gordonian Wisdom

In our home, we have traditionally introduced peanut butter around 12 months old. I was never impressed by "the wait until three years" evidence and we do not have a family history of food allergies. Our sixth child was fed a peanut butter sandwich at nine months by his babysitting older sister. Our youngest has had some peanut butter cooked into other foods, but not a peanut butter sandwich (that I know of). I'm sure we will serve her a PB&J as she gets closer to 12 months. Peanut butter is a major allergen, and it also poses a choking hazard. It should be introduced with caution.

Ideally, new foods should be introduced during a weekday when you can observe your child for a few hours and call your doctor if there are any problems. It is best to have liquid Benadryl (diphenhydramine) in your home prior to introducing the major food allergens. When you do decide to feed your child a peanut butter sandwich, spread the peanut butter thinly.

Should Children get a Daily Vitamin?

We do not give vitamins to our children. Health can not be found in a pill. We eat a variety of fresh foods (especially fruits and veggies) and encourage an outdoor lifestyle. Medical evidence does not support the use of vitamins in healthy individuals eating a variety of foods. (Pregnancy and infancy may be exceptions to this statement).

I do recommend vitamins for children with extremely limited diets. In those cases, vitamins should only be given during the transition to a healthy lifestyle.

Choking Hazards

Parents are right to worry about choking. Avoid hard candies, nuts, whole grapes, clumps of raisins, popcorn and anything of similar size and consistency. We introduce raisins, popcorn, whole grapes and some nuts when our children are three years old. When giving any child these things, they should be seated and calm. There is considerable variability in the size and shape of these chokeables. Anything can be a choking hazard when a child is running around.

In my practice, I frequently find parents who suffer from "fear of choking." These parents are unable to advance their child's diet to table foods because they worry that their child will choke. These parents can only hold out so long, as children become increasingly interested in table food. Many children will begin to scream and demand to be served table foods.

Getting Children to Eat Their Veggies

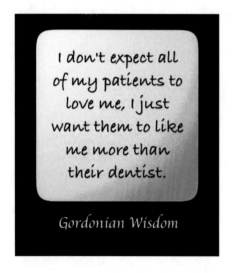

I don't expect all of my patients to love me, I just want them to like me more than their dentist.

Gordonian Wisdom

As a child, I was the picky eater of our family. My parents often joke that I survived my early years only because of peanut butter and jelly sandwiches. When dating my wife, my parents chuckled as they watched her serve me previously taboo veggies (like green pepper). It's funny how, given the right motivation, veggies really are "not that bad."

Like most parents, I wanted my children to adopt better eating habits. Fortunately, my children are great eaters, in large part, thanks to my wife. I marvel when my 4-year-old gets a second helping of asparagus, and the whole clan looks forward to artichoke night. We have built this foundation by setting a good example and through old fashioned persistence.

I reject the popular notion that health can be found in a pill or supplement. Get your exercise and eat a variety of healthy foods. At check-up visits, my patients have learned to expect questions about their fruit and veggie intake.

Parents often report that when their child tries to eat vegetables, they gag or even vomit. This is 100 percent psychological and is common. This is a behavioral problem. If you let this behavior dissuade you from serving a healthy diet, your child's diet and resistance will only worsen.

Currently, there is a popular cookbook on how to sneak vegetables into your child's diet. While I am not against it, this can't be the only approach. Eventually, your children will learn there is no Tooth Fairy and Mommy is putting broccoli in the muffins. The goal is to establish a healthy lifestyle for your children that will last a lifetime. This can only be accomplished if the child is aware of what he is eating.

Four Ideas to Improve your Family's Vegetable Intake

1) Serve Them

As parents, we often get tired of having our children throw food away or cry about it on their plates. If you want your children to eat healthy foods, you must repetitively present them with healthy foods. You must set a good example and eat your own fruits and veggies. One of the big mistakes parents make is cooking a separate meal for their children. When possible, eat together as a family and turn off the TV.

Eight children into parenting, we are still learning. Before our seventh was a year old, we began serving him salad. He neither wanted to eat it, nor had the molars to chew it. He learned to expect salad on his plate and watched his family members eat their salads. Over the subsequent year, he learned to eat and enjoy his salads.

<u>A Starting Point for the Parents of Picky Eaters</u>

Complete the sentence - "I would just be happy if they ate _____." As adults, we cannot eat for dinner what we had for lunch. Children are different. Most kids would prefer to eat the same foods over and over. If you want them to eat it - serve it and keep serving it. If your spouse is complaining you are serving _____ too often, you are right on track.

By simply setting a good example and recurrently presenting them with fruits and veggies, most children will adopt a healthy diet.

2) Serve Veggies as Appetizers

Try cutting up an apple (or other fruit or veggie) right before lunch. Call them to the table and ask what they would like for lunch. While you prepare their lunch, they sit in front of the fruit. Just like the chips at a Mexican restaurant - they're going to eat them.

At dinnertime, cut them and leave them on the kitchen countertop. As the smell of dinner cooking fills the house, they will be encouraged to chomp on a few veggies.

Mixed veggie trays are often a big hit. Try serving cut up carrots, celery, red pepper or broccoli with ranch dressing. Some kids just like to dip.

3) Make Veggies the Key to Dessert

My wife and I both grew up in homes where we had to "clear our plate" to get dessert. Our rule is you have to eat your vegetables to get dessert. This works great for children three years old and up.

Getting started

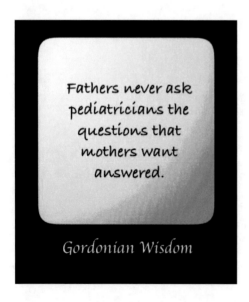

Fathers never ask pediatricians the questions that mothers want answered.

Gordonian Wisdom

Make a variety of cookie doughs and save them in the freezer in family sized servings. Before dinner, have your child help you place them on the pan and explain that everyone who eats their broccoli will get to have a cookie. Serve your child a tiny piece of broccoli. You can remind your child of the rule only once or twice toward the end of the meal. If your child does not eat his broccoli, then plates are cleared and the child must sit at the table and watch everyone else eat their cookies. For this approach to work, the child will have to fail at least once or twice. It is important that you declare the end of the meal and proceed with dessert. The child cannot be allowed to try again after the meal has ended. IF you do not place a defined end to your meals, then your meals will drag on forever. There needs to be a specific consequence at a specific time.

4) Plant a Garden

Now is a great time to plant a garden. Start them in pots so you can bring them inside during cold weather. Children who grow veggies are more likely to eat them. I recommend planting something that they can eat in the garden or on the dinner table. Grape tomatoes or snap peas are great suggestions. Avoid the use of chemicals so that they can eat them right after they are picked.

Be the person you want your children to become. If you want your children to adopt a healthy lifestyle, then you need to demonstrate one. Take care of yourself, exercise and eat your veggies.

Extended Breastfeeding

Parent Question:

What are your thoughts on extended breastfeeding (breastfeeding beyond one year of age)?

Clearly, the American Academy of Pediatrics recommendation of 12 months is an arbitrary time period. Most children wean as they get better at eating solid foods. Most of our children lost interest between 9 to 15 months. One of our daughters did nurse until two years old. It simply seemed "right" for her. After a year, she nursed only a couple times a day and was even able to skip days.

In my practice, I do not tell mothers to stop nursing. The duration of breastfeeding is a personal, family decision. The media has recently given a great deal of attention to mothers nursing children four years old or older. I am concerned that this is being done more for the mother and less for the child. Breastfeeding should be done with a child's best interest in mind.

Weaning Pacifiers

Between 9 to 12 months, it is time to begin to wean off pacifiers. Shortly after 12 months, pacifiers should disappear from "public view." Pacifiers after 12 months should be reserved for falling asleep, car rides, stressful situations (like doctors' visits) and places where quiet is necessary (church or a wedding). Pacifiers should completely be weaned around two years of age.

 Begin to decrease your child's pacifier use by 12 months.

Like most adults, I dislike seeing children over two years old with a pacifier. If your child can hold his "paci" like a cigarette, or talk around it he is too old for a pacifier. I often see 2- and 3-year-olds with overbites secondary to excessive or prolonged pacifier use.

Our oldest son was probably our most pacifier-addicted child. He slept with one in his mouth and one in each hand. At one year old, we struggled to wean his use. Finally, we tied his pacifier to a chair in the kitchen and told him he could have it all he wanted. It was great entertainment for my wife and I, as he would play for a while and then return to his pacifier to "gas up."

When we were ready to discontinue the pacifier, we would clip the end of the pacifier with scissors. It only takes a small clip for the child to notice and refuse. We would let the child know that the pacifier was broken. After two or three days, our children moved on and never had thumb-sucking or other "oral" issues (at least not yet).

Our seventh child was born during a high maintenance phase for his older brother, Ben. Ben was 22 months, fussy and whiny when our seventh was born. Maggie informed me that we would not be taking our 22-month-old's pacifier away. I'm not the brightest, but I have learned not to argue with an exhausted, pregnant woman. I was worried about this plan, as it is hard to take away a child's pacifiers when there are other pacifiers in the home. We did take the time to explain to Ben that, "Pacifiers are for babies."

One night, shortly after our newborn came home from the hospital, Ben began calling for me after he was already in bed. I remember Maggie was nursing the baby when I went into Ben's room. I expected that his pacifiers had fallen out of his crib or that he wanted a drink of water. When I went into his room, Ben was holding his pacifiers and saying, "Pacis baby." I asked, "Do you want to give your pacis to the baby?" He said, "Yes." I took Ben out of his crib, he walked and gave all his pacifiers to his newborn brother. He quit cold turkey! He did not need a pacifier that night and did not reclaim his pacifiers the next day.

Final Thoughts

In practice, I often find families that were unaware of the issues that they need to address. Many parents only begin to think about teaching their child to sleep through the night after learning their friends' baby is already sleeping. Months of bad habits make the process more difficult. I hope my book helps families address these common, preventable issues. Early knowledge and awareness of potential problems help parents address most parenting pitfalls.

As parents of eight children, we have daily moments to rejoice and struggle. When one of our children earns all A's at school, another is struggling in math. During the time of writing this book, our family had many down times. Often amid our family chaos, Maggie would look at me and ask, "Are you sure you should be writing a parenting book?" I learned to reply by asking, "Are you worried about the baby?" The answer was always, "No." Eight children into it, "the early years" seem easy. The stress is gone and replaced by joy. Babies are a lot of work, but the work is easier when you are confident and aware of common challenges.

My intent in writing a parenting book was to write the book we wish we had for our first child - a practical book with specific examples and stories to create a knowledge and awareness of common parenting issues. Parenting is stressful. Parents frequently doubt their own abilities. Hopefully, this book will make your first year more enjoyable and less stressful.

Bibliography

Bialocerkowski, A. PhD BAppSc (Physio) MAppSc (Physio), Vladusic, S. BPhty, Ng, C MBBS BMedSci, "Prevalence, risk factors, and natural history of positional plagiocephaly: a systematic review," Dev Med Child Neurology, 1 AUG 2008.

Butler-O'Hara M, LeMoine C, Guillet R. Analgesia for neonatal circumcision: a randomized controlled trial of EMLA cream versus dorsal penile nerve block. Pediatrics. 1998;101(4).

Gerard CM, Physiologic studies on swaddling: an ancient child care practice which may promote supine position for infant sleep, J Pediatr 2002.

Greer, F MD, Sicherer, S, MD, Burks, A, MD, and the Committee on Nutrition and Section on Allergy and Immunology, Pediatrics Vol. 121 No. 1 January 1, 2008 ,pp. 183 -191.

Herschel M, Khoshnood B, Ellman C, Maydew N, Mittendorf R. Male circumcision: Global Trends and Determinants of Prevalence, Safety and Acceptablility. Neonatal circumcision. Randomized trial of a sucrose pacifier for pain control. Arch Pediatr Adolesc Med. 1998;152:279-284.

Huang, F., Nowak-Wegrzyn, A., "Early Consumption of Peanuts in Infancy Is Associated with a Low Prevalence of Peanut Allergy", Pediatrics Vol. 124 No. Supplement 2 November 1, 2009 pp. S118 -S119.

Kaufman GE, Cimo S, Miller LW, Blass EM. Department of Obstetrics and Gynecology, Boston Medical Center, Mass, USA. An evaluation of the effects of sucrose on neonatal pain with 2 commonly used circumcision methods.

Am J Obstet Gynecol. 2002 Mar;186(3):564-8.

Kurtis, P. MD, DeSilva, H. MBBS, Bernstein, B. PhD, Malakh, L. BA, Schechter, N. MD, A Comparison of the Mogen and Gomco Clamps in Combination With Dorsal Penile Nerve Block in Minimizing the Pain of Neonatal Circumcision. Pediatrics Vol 103 No 2 February 1, 1999 pp e23.

Kutlu A "Congenital dislocation of the hip and its relation to swaddling used in Turkey." J Pediatric Orthopedics 1992.

Palmer LS, Palmer JS. Rainbow Babies and Children's Hospital, Cleveland, Ohio, USA. Urology. 2008 Jul;72(1):68-71. Epub 2008 May 2. The efficacy of topical betamethasone for treating phimosis: a comparison of two treatment regimens.

Poole, J MD, Barriga, K MSPH, Leung, D MD,PhD, Hoffman, M RN, Eisenbarth MD,PhD, Rewers, M MD,PhD, Norris, J MPH,PhD, Timing of Initial Exposure to Cereal Grains and the Risk of Wheat Allergy,Pediatrics. 2006 Jun;117(6):2175-82.

Ponsky LE, Ross JH, Knipper N, Kay R   Department of Urology, Cleveland Clinic Foundation, Cleveland, Ohio. Penile adhesions after neonatal circumcision.   JOURNAL OF UROLOGY, Volume 164, Number 2: Pages 495-496, August 2000.

Ponsonby AL, Dwyer, T, Gibbons, LE, Cochrane, J, Wang Y "Factor potentiating the risk of sudden infant death syndrome associated with prone position. New England Journal of Medicine August 5 1993.

Richardson HL "Minimizing the risks of sudden infant death syndrome: To swaddle or not to swaddle?" J Pediatr 2009.

Seither, R. MPH, Shaw, L. MS, Knighton, C., Greby, S. DVM, Stokley, S. MPH, Vaccination Coverage Among Children in Kindergarten — United States, 2012–13 School Year, August 2, 2013 / 62(30);607-612.

Taddio, A. BScPhm, PhD, Ohlsson, A. MD, MSc, FRCPC, Einarson, T PhD, Stevens, B. RN, PhD, Koren, G. MD, FRCPC, A Systematic Review of Lidocaine-Prilocaine Cream (EMLA) in the Treatment of Acute Pain in Neonates, Pediatrics, Vol. 101 No. 2 February 1, 1998.

Weiss, H., Larke, N., Halperin, D., and Schenker, I. Complications of circumcision in male neonates, infants and children: a systematic review. BMC Urology 2010, February 16. doi: 10.1186/1471-2490-10-2.

Wilson CA, "Clothing and bedding and its relevance to sudden infant death syndrome." J Paedriatr Child Health 1994.